C000130685

WITHDRAWN
FROM STOCK

LIVERPOOL
UNIVERSITY LIBRARY
————
OVERNIGHT OR
WEEKEND LOAN
ONLY

THE UNIVERS
HAROLD (

BIOMEDICA
C

Books issued over
0.30 a.m. the f
ssued for the week
0.30 . Monday
ayak late r t

COMPUTABILITY THEORY
Concepts and Applications

ELLIS HORWOOD SERIES IN COMPUTERS AND THEIR APPLICATIONS

Series Editor: IAN CHIVERS, Senior Analyst, The Computer Centre, King's College, London, and formerly Senior Programmer and Analyst, Imperial College of Science and Technology, University of London

Abramsky, S. & Hankin, C.J.	ABSTRACT INTERPRETATION OF DECLARATIVE LANGUAGES
Alexander, H.	FORMALLY-BASED TOOLS AND TECHNIQUES FOR HUMAN–COMPUTER DIALOGUES
Atherton, R.	STRUCTURED PROGRAMMING WITH BBC BASIC
Atherton, R.	STRUCTURED PROGRAMMING WITH COMAL
Baeza-Yates, R.A.	TEXT SEARCHING ALGORITHMS
Bailey, R.	FUNCTIONAL PROGRAMMING WITH HOPE
Barrett, R., Ramsay, A. & Sloman, A.	POP-11
Berztiss, A.	PROGRAMMING WITH GENERATORS
Bharath, R.	COMPUTERS AND GRAPH THEORY
Bishop, P.	FIFTH GENERATION COMPUTERS
Bullinger, H.-J. & Gunzenhauser, H.	SOFTWARE ERGONOMICS
Burns, A.	NEW INFORMATION TECHNOLOGY
Carberry, J.C.	COBOL
Carlini, U. & Villano, U.	TRANSPUTERS AND PARALLEL ARCHITECTURES
Chivers, I.D.	AN INTRODUCTION TO STANDARD PASCAL
Chivers, I.D.	MODULA 2
Chivers, I.D. & Sleighthome, J.	INTERACTIVE FORTRAN 77
Clark, M.W.	PC-PORTABLE FORTRAN
Clark, M.W.	TEX
Cockshott, W. P.	A COMPILER WRITER'S TOOLBOX: How to Implement Interactive Compilers for PCs with Turbo Pascal
Cockshott, W. P.	PS-ALGOL IMPLEMENTATIONS: Applications in Persistent Object-Oriented Programming
Colomb, R.	IMPLEMENTING PERSISTENT PROLOG
Cope, T.	COMPUTING USING BASIC
Curth, M.A. & Edelmann, H.	APL
Dahlstrand, I.	SOFTWARE PORTABILITY AND STANDARDS
Dandamudi, S. P.	HIERARCHICAL HYPERCUBE MULTICOMPUTER INTERCONNECTION NETWORKS
Dongarra, J., Duff, I., Gaffney, P., & McKee, S.	VECTOR AND PARALLEL COMPUTING
Dunne, P.E.	COMPUTABILITY THEORY: Concepts and Applications
Eastlake, J.J.	A STRUCTURED APPROACH TO COMPUTER STRATEGY
Eisenbach, S.	FUNCTIONAL PROGRAMMING
Ellis, D.	MEDICAL COMPUTING AND APPLICATIONS
Ennals, J.R.	ARTIFICIAL INTELLIGENCE
Ennals, J.R.	BEGINNING MICRO-PROLOG
Ennals, J.R., *et al.*	INFORMATION TECHNOLOGY AND EDUCATION
Filipič, B.	PROLOG USER'S HANDBOOK
Ford, N.	COMPUTER PROGRAMMING LANGUAGES
Ford, N.J., Ford, J.M., Holman, D.F. & Woodroffe, M.R.	COMPUTERS AND COMPUTER APPLICATIONS: An Introduction for the 1990s
Grill, E.	RELATIONAL DATABASES
Grune, D. & Jacobs, C.J.H.	PARSING TECHNIQUES: A Practical Guide
Guariso, G. & Werthner, H.	ENVIRONMENTAL DECISION SUPPORT SYSTEMS
Harland, D.M.	CONCURRENCY AND PROGRAMMING LANGUAGES
Harland, D.M.	POLYMORPHIC PROGRAMMING LANGUAGES
Harland, D.M.	REKURSIV
Harris, D.J.	DEVELOPING DEDICATED DBASE SYSTEMS
Henshall, J. & Shaw, S.	OSI EXPLAINED, 2nd Edition
Hepburn, P.H.	FURTHER PROGRAMMING IN PROLOG
Hepburn, P.H.	PROGRAMMING IN MICRO-PROLOG MADE SIMPLE
Hill, I.D. & Meek, B.L.	PROGRAMMING LANGUAGE STANDARDISATION
Hirschheim, R., Smithson, S. & Whitehouse, D.	MICROCOMPUTERS AND THE HUMANITIES: Survey and Recommendations
Hutchins, W.J.	MACHINE TRANSLATION
Hutchison, D.	FUNDAMENTALS OF COMPUTER LOGIC
Hutchison, D. & Silvester, P.	COMPUTER LOGIC
Koopman, P.	STACK COMPUTERS
Koops, A. & J. Dreijklufft	WORKING WITH COREL DRAW!
Kenning, M.-M. & Kenning, M.J.	COMPUTERS AND LANGUAGE LEARNING: Current Theory and Practice
Koskimies, K. & Paaki, J.	AUTOMATING LANGUAGE IMPLEMENTATION
Koster, C.H.A.	TOP-DOWN PROGRAMMING WITH ELAN
Last, R.	ARTIFICIAL INTELLIGENCE TECHNIQUES IN LANGUAGE LEARNING
Lester, C.	A PRACTICAL APPROACH TO DATA STRUCTURES

COMPUTABILITY THEORY
Concepts and Applications

PAUL E. DUNNE
Department of Computer Science, Liverpool University

ELLIS HORWOOD
NEW YORK   LONDON   TORONTO   SYDNEY   TOKYO   SINGAPORE

First published in 1991 by
ELLIS HORWOOD LIMITED
Market Cross House, Cooper Street,
Chichester, West Sussex, PO19 1EB, England

A division of
Simon & Schuster International Group
A Paramount Communications Company

© Ellis Horwood Limited, 1991

All rights reserved. No part of this publication may be reproduced, stored in a
retrieval system, or transmitted, in any form, or by any means, electronic, mechanical,
photocopying, recording or otherwise, without the prior permission, in writing, of the
publisher

Printed and bound in Great Britain
by Hartnolls Limited, Bodmin, Cornwall

British Library Cataloguing in Publication Data

Paul E. Dunne
Computability theory: concepts and applications
CIP catalogue record for this book is available from the British Library
ISBN 0–13–161936–5 (Library Edn.)
ISBN 0–13–159484–2 (Student Pbk. Edn.)

Library of Congress Cataloging-in-Publication Data available

Contents

Preface

I don't quite know whether it would be arrogant of me to take the blame on the grounds that it was I who initiated it ... My own contribution probably seems more important than it is because, as I say, it was my small contribution which set it all going as it were — and yet, if it comes to that, which of you with a shot or two of benzedrine couldn't have done as well or better?

N.F. Simpson
A Resounding Tinkle

This book is intended for use as a textbook for introductory courses covering Computability Theory. It has its origins in a final year undergraduate course that has been taught in the Department of Computer Science at Liverpool University for a number of years.

With the number of textbooks already available covering this field, the reader may well be justified in asking whether any useful purpose is served with the production of yet another one. In answer to this I would cite the two main difficulties students on our course have encountered when alternative texts have been recommended as source material. Neither of these concern the technical merits of other works on Computability Theory; they are more a reflection of the way in which our course has developed and of the background knowledge possessed by a typical student undertaking it. The history of the course taught at Liverpool and my personal view of the subject have resulted in a particular syllabus covering a number of diverse relevant aspects of Computability e.g. the matrix mortality problem is included, not because it is an intrinsically important problem, but rather because it provides an interesting example of a simple, unsolvable, computational problem that is more 'natural' than problems based on the behaviour of programs. Given that Computability is a vast subject and that no two authors will have exactly the same view of what ought to be taught, there has been no single textbook available that covers all the material in the current syllabus. Diversity of syllabi will be a problem with any textbook on most courses and thus the most that this book can hope to do is offer a different syllabus that may be found more in keeping with the requirements of certain courses. The second difficulty with most existing texts arises out of the fact that the course is taught to Computer Science students by a Computer Science Department: although all those studying the subject have a reasonable background in mathematics their primary interests are non-mathematical. In consequence a number of current works on Computability Theory are unsuitable partly because their presentation is found to be technically too demanding but mainly because there is little attempt to relate the material covered to relevant concerns within Computer Science.

Computability theory is an important area of Computer

Science and one which, I feel, ought to be a required aspect of any first degree course in the subject. While realising that it is impossible to produce something satisfying everyone in terms of syllabus content, my aim in putting together this book has been largely to present the material from a Computer Science viewpoint. To this end I have tried to motivate and expand on the more important results proved while avoiding any excessive mathematicisation of the material.

A number of students have commented on earlier versions of this text when it was circulated as a set of lecture notes. I can take this opportunity to thank all of those who suggested ways of improving the presentation of particular results and who pointed out mistakes; it should go without saying that all remaining errors are my sole responsibility. In addition, I would like to thank Mike Paterson who provided a number of valuable comments on the first draft of this book. Finally, I would like to thank my colleagues in the Department of Computer Science at Liverpool University for their incisive criticism of certain draft chapters, in particular Jim Watt who provided a number of suggestions concerning the content.

P.E.D

Liverpool, February 1991

Chapter 1

Introduction

It's nothing to do with the question of intelligence. It's a way of being able to look at the world. It's a question of how far you can operate on things and not in things. I mean it's a question of your capacity to ally the two, to relate the two, to balance the two.

Harold Pinter
The Homecoming

This book is concerned with properties of computers and in particular limits on their ability to solve problems. In practice we may often encounter such limitations on computational power as inadequate speed, so that some tasks cannot be carried out since the fastest programs to deal with them take too long to terminate, or insufficient memory when the working space needed to solve a problem exceeds the amount available. The field of computational complexity theory is partly concerned with identifying problems for which even the best possible programs are impracticable because of such excessive resource requirements. In this book, however, we deal with a much more fundamental limitation on computational power: problems which cannot be solved by computer programs no matter how much time and memory is provided. In other words there are problems for which it may be *mathematically proved* that 'effective' algorithms for solving them do not exist. The investigation of problems of this kind forms the core of the discipline of *Computability*, or *Recursive Function Theory*.

The study of Computability Theory as a formal mathematical discipline originated almost fifty years before the appearance of the first digital computers and has its roots in the work of Hilbert, Gödel, Rosser, Kleene, Church, Turing and Post concerning the power of mathematical reasoning with respect to a *computational* problem posed by Hilbert in 1900. The contribution of Gödel, and subsequently Rosser, to this field led to the famous Incompleteness Theorem published in 1931 by Gödel. In simple terms this established that no mathematical reasoning system has sufficient potency to be capable of *proving* every true assertion about the properties of natural numbers. A simplified development of Gödel's work will be given in Chapters 9 and 10 below.

Kleene, Church, Turing and Post independently devised differing formalisations for the concept of 'effective algorithm'. As we shall see below all of these definitions turn out to be equivalent: e.g. the programming system proposed by Turing in 1936 — described in the next chapter — can be simulated by the programming system devised by Post in 1936 and vice versa. These equivalences motivate the important Church-Turing hypothesis which is discussed in Chapter 3. Informally this asserts that the class of problems that can be solved using Turing's programming system is exactly the same as the class that can be solved using any 'reasonable' programming system: i.e those problems which would be 'intuitively regarded' as solvable. The universal acceptance of the Church-Turing hypothesis provides the necessary basis for a definition of the concepts *effective algorithm* and *solvable problem*.

Although the formal treatment of computability issues is a development of 20th century mathematics, the search for effective algorithms to solve certain problems dates back over 2000 years: ancient Greek mathematics, as is evident in the work of Euclid and Pythagoras, placed great emphasis on constructive techniques. In geometry three classical problems, one of which remained unsolved until the end of the 19th century, were the subject of much investigation: squaring the circle, trisecting an angle, and duplicating the cube. For these it was required to devise sequences of steps, to be carried out using only a ruler and a pair of compasses, that would respectively: given a circle, produce a square of exactly the same area; given any angle, divide it into three equal angles; given a cube, construct another with exactly twice the volume of the original. In this context 'effective algorithms' are those whose 'computational' steps employ only ruler and compasses; hence the three problems are all concerned with finding algorithms belonging within a specific programming system or exhibiting a proof that no such algorithm exists. It is now known that appropriate constructive methods do not exist for any of the three problems. One can show that the length of any line segment constructed using ruler and compasses may be written as an expression involving only natural numbers and the operations $+$, $\times$, $\div$ and $\sqrt{\ }$: duplicating the cube is impossible since it requires constructing a line of length $2^{1/3}$; the angular trisection problem involves constructing lines whose lengths are given by the roots of a cubic polynomial — for certain angles such as $60°$ these lengths are not expressible in the required form.   Both of these results were established by Descartes in 1637. The impossibility of squaring the circle was finally shown in 1882 by Lindemann who proved that π was transcendental and therefore, since any solution must construct a line of length $\sqrt{\pi}$ which could not be written as a suitable expression, no valid algorithm exists.

Computability Theory is concerned with constructing a mathematical formalism for reasoning about the existence or non-existence of effective algorithms for particular problems. Any mathematical theory of computation should aim to be as general as possible. The results proved within it should be applicable to all computer architectures, regardless of differing parameters such as instruction set, processor speed and memory size. For this reason one must avoid constructing a theory based on any specific computer architecture operating in a particular environment since any results proved for such instances may not hold for other configurations. To achieve this objective, Computability Theory uses as its basis the concept of *models of computation*. These are abstract mathematical models of stored program computers that encapsulate intuitive notions of computer operation. A number of models of computation will be encountered in this text ranging from generalisations of *finite automata* (such as *Turing machines*) to *string manipulation* methods, such as *Post machines* and *Markov algorithms*. By employing these formal devices we can make precise the intuitive ideas of effective algorithm and solvable problem.

Before examining the issue of computability we need to develop a rigorous formulation of what is meant by a 'problem'. Consider the behaviour of any computer program: some input (which may be none at all) is read and using this some output is generated. Usually the input is required to meet certain constraints[†]. At this level of abstraction it is clear that any program may be regarded as evaluating a *function*, *f*, which maps from some *domain* of input values, *I*, to some *range* of output values, *O*. For example with a high-level programming language compiler; *I = character files*, *O = binary files*. In this way it is sufficiently general to examine the question: 'Which problems can be solved by computer programs?' via the *equivalent* question 'Which functions can be computed?'.

This viewpoint is still slightly unsatisfactory since the terms 'domain' and 'range' could be loosely interpreted in a number of different ways, e.g. should the domain for a compiler be considered as the set of all syntactically correct programs — which has the advantage that each input yields a definite output — or should it consist of all character files — in which case some inputs will not produce a binary output? Similarly how should the term 'file' be defined? The disadvantage of permitting too broad a definition of these terms is that it may become necessary to consider a different variation of the function represented by a program for each different computer the program is run on and so one no longer has a general model. It is therefore preferable to refine the concept of function further by abstracting the ideas of 'domain' and 'range' so as to avoid use of terms such as 'file'. The following allows us to do this.

Definition 1.1: An *alphabet* is a finite set of symbols. Σ will denote an arbitrary alphabet. One particular case we will be interested in is $\Sigma = \{0,1\}$. For any alphabet Σ, Σ^* denotes the set of all finite strings of symbols from Σ. Any

---

† It is, of course, unnecessary to consider computations which return no 'result' whatsoever: in terms of the abstraction presented below computability, for such functions, is a somewhat trivial issue.

such string is called a *word*. Σ^n (for n a whole number) denotes the set of all words which contain exactly n symbols. Σ^* contains a word ϵ which contains no symbols. This is called the *empty* word. For x in Σ^* the *length* of x, denoted $|x|$, is the number of symbols occurring in x, thus $|\epsilon| = 0$. Let x and y be words in Σ^*: x *concatenated with* y is the word formed by the symbols of x followed by the symbols of y. This is denoted by $x.y$ (or sometimes just xy) and has length $|x| + |y|$. •

Example 1.1: The following are examples of alphabets:

i.   *Binary* = $\{0, 1\}$.

ii.   *Roman* = $\{A,B,C,D,E,F, \ldots , X,Y,Z\}$.

iii.   *Greek* = $\{\alpha, \beta, \gamma, \delta, \varepsilon, \ldots , \chi, \psi, \omega, A, \ldots , \Omega\}$.

iv.   *Decimal* = $\{0,1,2,3,4,5,6,7,8,9\}$.

The set of words in *Binary** is a proper subset of the set of words in *Decimal** e.g. the words 100, 010, 1 and 10010011 occur in both sets, but the words 900, 0513345923 and 2 occur only in *Decimal**. Similarly *Roman** contains the words *LIVERPOOL, COMPUTABILITY, XXXX* and *STUDENT*; *Greek** the words $\overset{\cdot}{A}\phi\rho o\delta\iota\tau\eta$, $\overset{\cdot}{\varepsilon}\rho\omega\tau\alpha$, $\gamma\upsilon\nu\eta$, $K\upsilon\theta\varepsilon\rho\alpha$ and $\tau\iota\mu\eta$.

Binary^2 contains exactly the words $\{00,01,10,11\}$. The lengths of the words 1010, 2, *HIBERNIAN* and $\overset{\cdot}{\alpha}\gamma\alpha\pi\eta$ are, respectively 4, 2, 9 and 5. Finally the result of concatenating the words 123 and 456 is the word 123456 in *Decimal**. •

Using alphabets and words over alphabets we can concentrate on functions $f : \Sigma_1^* \rightarrow \Sigma_2^*$, where Σ_1 and Σ_2 are alphabets.

Finally we can make one further refinement.

Definition 1.2: A *decision problem* is a function whose result is either 0 or 1 (equivalently **false** or **true**). So all functions $f:\Sigma^* \rightarrow \{0,1\}$ are decision problems over Σ. •

Example 1.2: The following are examples of decision problems over the alphabets in Example 1.1:

i. *EVEN* : *Binary* $^* \rightarrow \{0,1\}$: *EVEN*(x) is **true** if and only if the word x ends with the symbol 0 i.e. the binary number encoded by x is even. Hence *EVEN*(00110) = 1 but *EVEN*(111) = 0.

ii. *Palind* : *Roman* $^* \rightarrow \{0,1\}$: *Palind*(x) equals 1 if and only if the word x is a palindrome. Therefore *Palind*(*MINIM*) is **true** but *Palind*(*STOP*) is **false**.

iii. *Iliad* : *Greek* $^* \rightarrow \{0,1\}$: *Iliad*(x) = 1 if and only if the word x occurs in the (Greek) text of the Iliad. Hence *Iliad*($o\dot{v}\rho\alpha\nu o\nu$) = 1[†] whereas *Iliad*($K\alpha\lambda\upsilon\psi\omega$) = 0.

iv. *PRIME* : *Decimal* $^* \rightarrow \{0,1\}$: *PRIME*(x) is **true** if and only if the word x represents a decimal number which is prime; thus *PRIME*(37) is **true**, but *PRIME*(999) is **false**. •

Decision problems are problems concerned with determining if some property is true of the input.

Now consider any decision problem $f:\Sigma^* \rightarrow \{0,1\}$. Clearly Σ^* can be divided into two disjoint sets: the set of words $x \in \Sigma^*$ such that $f(x) = 1$; and the set of words $x \in \Sigma^*$ such that $f(x) = 0$. The former is called the *language* corresponding to f, and will be denoted by $L(f)$. The latter, $\Sigma^* - L(f)$, is called the *complement* of $L(f)$, denoted by $CO - L(f)$. Note that, in general, both $L(f)$ and $CO - L(f)$ will be infinite sets.

Example 1.3: Using the decision problems of Example 1.2 we have,

---

† e.g. $\Pi\eta\lambda\epsilon\iota\delta\eta\varsigma$ $\delta'\omega\mu\omega\xi\epsilon\nu$, $\iota\delta\omega\nu$ $\epsilon\iota\varsigma$ $o\dot{v}\rho\alpha\nu o\nu$ $\epsilon\dot{v}\rho\upsilon\nu$ (Book XXI, line 272)

i. $L(EVEN) = \{0, 00, 10, 000, 010, 100, 110, \ldots, \}$ and
     $CO-L(EVEN) = \{1, 01, 11, 001, 011, 101, 111, \ldots, \}$.

ii. $L(Palind)$ contains the words *AVA*, *MINIM* and *BBBB*;
     $CO-L(Palind)$ contains the words *MARIA*, *BREVE* and
     XYXY.

iii. $L(Iliad)$ contains the words $\dot{\epsilon}\lambda\chi o\nu$, $\nu\nu\chi\tau\alpha$ and
     $\dot{\alpha}\rho o\upsilon\rho\alpha\nu;^\dagger$ $CO-L(Iliad)$ contains the words $\Pi\epsilon\rho\iota\kappa\lambda\eta\varsigma$,
     $N\alpha\upsilon\sigma\iota\kappa\alpha\alpha$ and $\dot{A}\epsilon\gamma\iota\sigma\theta\epsilon\upsilon\varsigma$. •

iv. $L(PRIME) = \{2, 3, 5, 7, 11, 13, 17, 19, 23, 29, \ldots, \}$ and
     $CO-L(PRIME) = \{1,4,6,8,9,10,12,14,15,16, \ldots, \}$. •

The important consequence of the preceding formalism is that we are now able to replace the vague idea of 'solving a problem' by the very precise concept of determining if a given input word is a member of a particular set of words. Thus to solve the problem of determining if a given natural number is prime is equivalent to deciding if it occurs in the set $\{2,3,5,7,11, \ldots, \}$.

The majority of our subsequent development will be concerned with the existence of effective algorithms for decision problems. The formal models of computation we consider all provide some basic set of operations for manipulating input data (compare instruction sets in stored program computers). It will be clear that the given operations are all 'computable' and thus an *effective algorithm* on some model for a given decision problem, f, is a sequence of (permitted) operations which determine whether or not any input x is in $L(f)$. Any such algorithm ($\equiv PROGRAM$) is said to *recognise* $L(f)$. Computability theory deals with dividing the universe of all languages over Σ^* into those which can be recognised by effective algorithms and those

† e.g. $\dot{\epsilon}\lambda\chi o\nu\ \nu\nu\chi\tau\alpha\ \mu\epsilon\lambda\alpha\iota\nu\alpha\nu\ \dot{\epsilon}\pi\iota\ \zeta\epsilon\iota\delta\omega\rho o\nu\ \dot{\alpha}\rho o\upsilon\rho\alpha\nu$ (Book VIII, line 486)

which cannot. In the context of the earlier discussion the latter correspond to non-computable functions, i.e. unsolvable problems.

Example 1.4: The following informally described algorithms can be used to recognise the languages of Example 1.3.

i.   For $x \in Binary^*$, check if x ends with the symbol 0.

ii. For $x \in Roman^*$ construct a new word y by reversing the order of the symbols in x; then check if $x = y$.

iii. Set up a dictionary of all words occurring in the Greek text of the Iliad and use this to check any given $x \in Greek^*$.

iv. Given $x \in Decimal^*$ for each natural number, y, between 2 and $x - 1$ test if y divides x without any remainder. If no y does so then x is prime.   •

Exercises

1. Let $\Sigma = \{A, B, C, D, E\}$.

i.   List all the words in Σ^2.

ii. List all the words in Σ^* which are words of the English language.

iii. How many distinct words does Σ^n contain.

2. Which of the languages of Example 1.3 are finite and which are infinite?

3. Informally describe how any finite language can be recognised.

Chapter 2

Turing machines

ἀμηχον τευχημα και δυσεκδυτον

Aeschylus
Fragment from unknown play[†]

The first formal model of computation was proposed by Alan Turing in 1936. Turing extrapolated the three basic components of any computer in defining this. Thus memory is modelled by providing a single infinite tape; input and output by a read/write head scanning this tape; processing by a simple device called a *finite control*. The infinitude of tape allows memory size restrictions, which are irrelevant to computability issues, to be ignored. Before giving the full technical definition of Turing machine we will first

[†] (Nauck: *Tragicorum Graecorum fragmenta*, 2nd Edition, (1889); Fragment 375); 'A device which cannot be ignored or avoided' (transl: author).

informally describe how it is organised.

A Turing machine may be viewed as a mechanism for solving decision problems and for computing functions over the natural numbers. In general we will concentrate on the former application. The workspace for a Turing machine consists of an infinite capacity memory each cell of which may hold a single item of data. Memory locations are numbered $1,2,3,4,\ldots,$. The data items are symbols from a given alphabet, of which only a specified subset of symbols may be written into memory locations. The input word is placed in the first few locations of the memory with the remaining cells containing a special symbol to denote the fact that they contain no data. This symbol, called the *blank*, cannot be *written* into any location. The memory is scanned by a read/write head, initially placed on the first location, and this head can obtain and update the contents of just a single location in any one computation step. In addition the head is not free to access any location immediately but can only refer to one which was adjacent to the location it accessed on its previous step. The movements of the head and the changes to the memory content are controlled entirely by the program run in the processor. This program consists of a finite sequence of numbered instructions that fall into one of two categories:

i.   *Halt* instructions which terminate execution of the program.

ii.   *Test* instructions which determine how the current memory location should be altered and which instruction should be executed next.

There are two types of halt instruction: *accept* and *reject*. The former corresponds to returning the answer 1 (or **true**) for the decision problem being solved by the program; the latter is equivalent to returning the answer 0 (or **false**).

Without loss of generality it will be assumed that any program contains a unique accepting instruction and a unique rejecting instruction; these we denote by A and R respectively. Now let $\Gamma = \{\gamma_1, \ldots, \gamma_k\}$ be the alphabet of data symbols used, with γ_k being the blank symbol. If $cloc$ denotes the number of the current location and $M[j]$ the content of the jth memory location then each test instruction has the form:

i: **if** $M[cloc] = \gamma_1$ **then**
    $M[cloc] := \delta_1^i$
    $cloc := cloc + D_1^i$
    goto i_1
  elif $M[cloc] = \gamma_2$ **then**
    $M[cloc] := \delta_2^i$
    $cloc := cloc + D_2^i$
    goto i_2
  elif $M[cloc] = \gamma_3$ **then**
    . . .
  else $\{M[cloc] = \gamma_k\}$
    $M[cloc] := \delta_k^i$
    $cloc := cloc + D_k^i$
    goto i_k
 fi

Here δ_j^i is a (writable) alphabet symbol; $D_j^i \in \{+1, -1\}$; and i_j is a numbered program instruction or A or R.

So in a single computation step the program reads the symbol currently being scanned and, depending on what this and the instruction number are, writes some symbol; moves the head to some adjacent location; and jumps to a given instruction. Conventionally the first instruction to be executed by the program is numbered 0.

Example 2.1: The following program accepts all words over

the alphabet $\{0,1\}$ which start with an even number of 0s followed by a 1.

    0: **if** $M[\,cloc\,] = 0$ **then**
            $M[\,cloc\,] := 1$; $cloc := cloc + 1$; **goto** 1
       elif $M[\,cloc\,] = 1$ **then**
            $M[\,cloc\,] := 1$; $cloc := cloc + 1$; **goto** A
       else
            $M[\,cloc\,] := 1$; $cloc := cloc + 1$; **goto** R
       fi
    1: **if** $M[\,cloc\,] = 0$ **then**
            $M[\,cloc\,] := 1$; $cloc := cloc + 1$; **goto** 0
       elif $M[\,cloc\,] = 1$ **then**
            $M[\,cloc\,] := 1$; $cloc := cloc + 1$; **goto** R
       else
            $M[\,cloc\,] := 1$; $cloc := cloc + 1$; **goto** R
       fi
   A: **accept**
   R: **reject** •

We can now give a formal definition of a Turing machine as,

Definition 2.1: A *Turing machine*, *M*, is denoted by an 8-tuple,

$$M = (Q, \Sigma, \Gamma, \delta, q_0, B, q_A, q_R)$$

where:

Q is a finite set of *states*.

Γ is the alphabet of *input* symbols.

$B \in \Gamma$ is the *blank* symbol.

$\Sigma \subseteq \Gamma - \{B\}$ is the alphabet of *output* symbols.

$\delta : Q \times \Gamma \rightarrow Q \times \Sigma \times \{L,R\}$ is the *state transition function*.

$q_0 \in Q$ is the *initial* state.

q_A, q_R ∈ Q are the *final* states.

M has a one-way infinite tape divided into *cells* numbered 1, 2, 3 , . . . , . The tape is scanned by a *head* which can read and print on a single cell at a time. The operation of M is supervised by a simple process called a *finite control*.

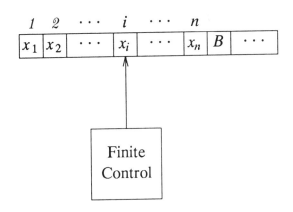

Figure 2.1: Single tape Turing machine

A Turing machine, M, computes as follows. Initially the state of the finite control is q_0 and the tape contains an input word $x_1 x_2 \cdots x_n \in (\Gamma - \{B\})^n$ in cells 1,2, . . . , n respectively. All other cells contain the blank symbol. The head is positioned at cell 1. In a single step or *move* M performs the following actions: the symbol on the tape cell scanned by the head is read; this, together with the current state, is used as an argument to δ, the state transition function, to determine the next state, which symbol is printed on the cell scanned and whether the head moves one cell left (L) or one cell right (R). The head is not permitted to move to the left of cell number 1. This process ceases when M enters one of the final states. If the state is q_A the input is said to be *accepted by M*; otherwise, if the final state is q_R, the input is said to be *rejected by M*.

Turing machines provide a model for evaluating

decision problems. For a given Turing machine, M, the set of words accepted from $(\Gamma - \{B\})^*$ is called the *language recognised* by M and is also denoted $L(M)$. •

In terms of our informal description given previously the tape is the infinite memory available, Γ is the alphabet of data symbols and Σ the subset of this which defines the writable data symbols. The states of a Turing machine are the labels of the instructions in the program executed by the processing agent. Note that the state transition function completely describes the *program* which controls the execution of a specific machine.

Example 2.2: The formal Turing machine description for the program described in Example 2.1 is given by:

$Q = \{q_0, q_1, q_A, q_R\}$

$\Gamma = \{0, 1, B\}$

$\Sigma = \{0, 1\}$

q_0 is the initial state.

q_A is the accepting state.

q_R the rejecting state.

B is the blank symbol.

The state transition function is

$\delta(q_0, 0) = (q_1, 1, R)$; $\delta(q_0, 1) = (q_A, 1, R)$

$\delta(q_0, B) = (q_R, 1, R)$; $\delta(q_1, 0) = (q_0, 1, R)$

$\delta(q_1, 1) = (q_R, 1, R)$; $\delta(q_1, B) = (q_R, 1, R)$

•

The functional form of a Turing machine program does not give a very clear view of the method by which a decision problem is solved. For describing particular Turing machine programs it is preferable to have some pictorial representation of the program behaviour. We can accomplish this by defining the *control graph* of a Turing machine.

Definition 2.2: Let $M = (Q, \Sigma, \Gamma, \delta, q_0, B, q_A, q_R)$ be a Turing machine. The *control graph* of M, denoted CG_M is a directed labelled graph in which there are labelled nodes corresponding to the set of states Q, each node being labelled with a unique state name. The edges of the graph are formed as follows. For each move $\delta(q_i, \sigma) = (q_j, \tau, D)$ (where $D \in \{L, R\}$) of M there is an edge from the node labelled q_i to the node labelled q_j in CG_M and this edge is labelled with a triple of the form $[\sigma; \tau; D]$. •

Example 2.3: The figure below gives the control graph for the Turing machine of Example 2.2.

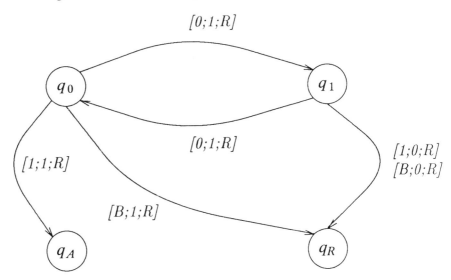

Figure 2.2: Turing machine control graph   •

Example 2.4: The control graph in Figure 2.3 describes a Turing machine which accepts only words of the form $0^n 1^n$. Its tape alphabet, Γ, consists of the symbols $\{0, 1, \#, \times, B\}$. The program operates by repeatedly: finding the leftmost occurrence of a 0 on the input tape; crossing this out, using the symbol #; finding the rightmost occurrence of a 1 on the tape; crossing this out, using the symbol ×. The process halts if the program fails to find a 1 when it expects to — in which case the input is rejected; or if there are no more occurrences of the symbol 0 and each 1 has been checked off — in which case the input is accepted. To simplify the description it is assumed that the initial input contains only the symbols 0 and 1.

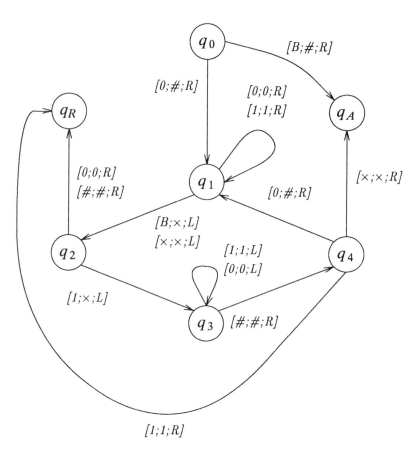

Figure 2.3: Turing machine recognising $0^n 1^n$ •

Another aid to visualising Turing machine operation, which is also useful as a notational device when proving properties of the behaviour of specific programs, is the concept of an *instantaneous description*.

Definition 2.3: Let M be a Turing machine and $\mathbf{x} = x_1...x_n \in \Gamma^*$ be an input word for M. An *instantaneous description* of M on input $\mathbf{x}$ is a word in $(\Gamma \cup Q)^*$ that describes the contents of the tape of M, its state and its head position. We use $ID_t(M, \mathbf{x})$ to denote the instantaneous description of M on $\mathbf{x}$ after t moves have been made (where $t \geq 0$). The word ID_t consists of three parts:

$$ID_t \;=\; Before \,.\, State \,.\, After$$

Suppose that t moves have been made by M, the first m cells are non-blank, the head is scanning cell number k, and M is in state q_i. If we use c_j to denote the contents of cell number j then

$$ID_t \;=\; c_1 c_2 \;\cdots\; c_{k-1} q_i c_k c_{k+1} \;\cdots\; c_{m+1}$$

In this way the *Before* section of ID_t gives the content of the tape cells to the left of the current cell; the *State* symbol both records the current state and indicates which cell is being scanned; the *After* section describes the content of the current cell and all cells to the right of this up to and including the first blank cell.

If ID_i and ID_j are two instantaneous descriptions for M on input $\mathbf{x}$ we say that ID_i *yields* ID_j, written $ID_i \rightarrowtail ID_j$, if and only if ID_j results from ID_i after a single move of M. Similarly ID_i is said to *derive* ID_j, denoted $ID_i \Rightarrow ID_j$, if and only if ID_j results from ID_i after some sequence of moves of M.   •

Example 2.5: For the machine described in Example 2.4 the sequence of instantaneous descriptions produced with input 0011 are as follows:

$$ID_0 = q_0 0011B \qquad ID_1 = \# q_1 011B$$
$$ID_2 = \# 0q_1 11B \qquad ID_3 = \# 01q_1 1B$$
$$ID_4 = \# 011q_1 B \qquad ID_5 = \# 01q_2 1 \times B$$
$$ID_6 = \# 0q_3 1 \times \times B \qquad ID_7 = \# q_3 01 \times \times B$$
$$ID_8 = q_3 \# 01 \times \times B \qquad ID_9 = \# q_4 01 \times \times B$$
$$ID_{10} = \# \# q_1 1 \times \times B \qquad ID_{11} = \# \# 1q_1 \times \times B$$
$$ID_{12} = \# \# q_2 1 \times \times B \qquad ID_{13} = \# q_3 \# \times \times \times B$$
$$ID_{14} = \# \# q_4 \times \times \times B \qquad ID_{15} = \# \# \times q_A \times \times B$$

•

Detailed constructions of Turing machines are generally cumbersome and tedious. It is convenient to have some armoury of techniques for designing Turing machines that allow some of the technical complications to be avoided. Two of the most useful methods are described below:

Storage in finite control

The notion of *state* can be used to allow some *finite* amount of information to be remembered; for example the last k symbols read, where k is some fixed constant. For this each $q \in Q$ would be viewed as a $k+1$-tuple, $<q_i, a_1, a_2, \ldots, a_k>$ where q_i is the 'state' for control purposes, and $a_1, \ldots, a_k$ the previous k symbols read. This records the information that M is in state q_i having just read $a_1, \ldots, a_k$. It is important to note that this is not a change in the definition of Turing machine, all that has happened is that the number of states (using finite storage) increases from $|Q|$ (the number of control states) to at most $|Q| . |\Gamma|^k$.

Multiple Tracks

The tape is considered as divided into *k tracks*, each track square recording one symbol. The head reads and prints *k*-tuples during moves. Again this is just a conceptual change and can be considered as replacing Γ by Γ^k and Σ by $\Gamma^k - (\Gamma - \Sigma)^k$.

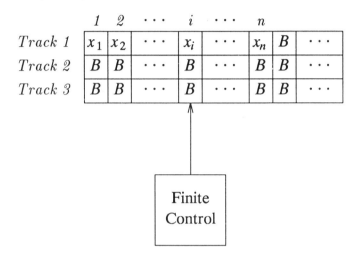

Figure 2.3: *3*-Track Turing machine

There are various modifications to the actual definition of Turing machine, which at first sight, may seem to yield models of greater power, i.e. machines able to solve more decision problems. Below we examine two such extensions and show that this appearance is illusory.

The first simple modification one might make is to permit a *two-way* infinite tape, with cells numbered $\cdots -2, -1, 0, 1, 2, \cdots$ (the input will be placed in cells $0, 1, \ldots, n-1$ initially). For any alphabet, Σ, let $1 - WAY(\Sigma)$ denote the set of languages over Σ^* that can be accepted by Turing machines having a one-way infinite tape; and $2 - WAY(\Sigma)$ denote the set of languages over Σ^* accepted by Turing machines with a two-way infinite tape.

Theorem 2.1: $\forall \; \Sigma \;\; 1\text{-}WAY(\Sigma) = 2\text{-}WAY(\Sigma)$

Proof: That $1\text{-}WAY(\Sigma) \subseteq 2\text{-}WAY(\Sigma)$ is obvious. For the reverse containment we use a *2*-track one-way infinite tape to record the contents of a two-way infinite tape. Suppose M_2 is a Turing machine with a two-way infinite tape. Let

$$M_2 \;\; = \;\; (Q, \; \Sigma_2, \; \Gamma_2, \; \delta_2, \; q_0, \; B_2, \; q_A, \; q_R)$$

We wish to construct an equivalent Turing machine, M_1, having one-way infinite tape, and satisfying $L(M_1) = L(M_2)$. So M_1 is a Turing machine with

$$M_1 \;\; = \;\; (S, \; \Sigma_1, \; \Gamma_1, \; \delta_1, \; s_0, \; B_1, \; s_A, \; s_R)$$

The figure below illustrates how the tape of M_1 records the information on the tape of M_2. The notation c_j indicates the symbol recorded on the *j*th square.

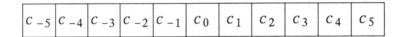

c_{-5}	c_{-4}	c_{-3}	c_{-2}	c_{-1}	c_0	c_1	c_2	c_3	c_4	c_5

Tape of M_2

c_0	c_1	c_2	c_3	c_4	c_5	$\cdots$
$\otimes$	c_{-1}	c_{-2}	c_{-3}	c_{-4}	c_{-5}	$\cdots$

Tape of M_1

Figure 2.4: Simulation of *2*-way infinite tape by *1*-way infinite tape

The special symbol $\otimes$ in the first cell of M_1 indicates that this is the leftmost tape cell. Informally when simulating the moves of M_2, the finite control of M_1 is used to indicate whether the top track or lower track holds the symbol which would be scanned by M_2. This can be accomplished by making the state set of S of M_1 contain $Q \times \{UT, LT\}$, so that if M_1 is in state $<q_i, UT>$, for example, then M_2 is in state q_i scanning a cell in the nonnegative section of its tape.

We complete the proof by giving a detailed description of how M_1 is built from M_2.

$$S = Q \times \{UT, LT\} \cup \{s_A, s_R\}$$
$$\Gamma_1 = \Gamma_2 \times (\Gamma_2 \cup \{\otimes\})$$
$$B_1 = (B_2, B_2)$$
$$\Sigma_1 = \Gamma_1 - \{B_1\}$$
$$s_0 = <q_0, UT>$$

For each move $\delta_2(q_i, \sigma) = (q_j, \tau, D)$ of M_2 there are moves:

$$\delta_1(<q_i, UT>, (\sigma, \alpha)) = (<q_j, UT>, (\tau, \alpha), D)$$

$$\delta_1(<q_i, LT>, (\alpha, \sigma)) = (<q_j, LT>, (\alpha, \tau), \neg D)$$

where $\neg D = L$ if $D = R$ and vice-versa. There are moves of this form in δ_1 for each $\alpha \in \Gamma_2$. If q_j is a halting state then δ_1 moves to the appropriate halting state s_A or s_R. The only moves remaining to be described are for the cases when M_1 would be scanning the first cell of its tape, i.e. an input of the form $(\alpha, \otimes)$ for some $\alpha \in \Gamma_2$. These are covered by the following rules for each of the possibilities:

$$\delta_2(q_i, \sigma) = (q_j, \tau, L)$$
$$\delta_2(q_i, \sigma) = (q_j, \tau, R)$$

In the first case we have moves

$$\delta_1(<q_i, UT>, <\sigma, \otimes>) = (<q_j, LT>, <\tau, \otimes>, R)$$
$$\delta_1(<q_i, LT>, <\sigma, \otimes>) = (<q_j, LT>, <\tau, \otimes>, R)$$

and in the second

$$\delta_1(<q_i, UT>, <\sigma, \otimes>) = (<q_j, UT>, <\tau, \otimes>, R)$$
$$\delta_1(<q_i, LT>, <\sigma, \otimes>) = (<q_j, UT>, <\tau, \otimes>, R)$$

This completes the proof of the theorem. □

The second modification is to increase the number of *tapes* from 1 to k for some fixed k. In a k-tape Turing machine, each of the k-tapes is scanned by its own read/write head. In a single move the symbol scanned by each head is read (in parallel) and these k symbols together with the current state are used to determine the next state, which symbol is printed by each head and whether a head moves left one square (L), right one square (R) or remains stationary (S). δ is now a function

$$\delta : Q \times \Gamma^k \;\rightarrow\; Q \times \Sigma^k \times \{L,R,S\}^k$$

For any alphabet Σ let $k-tape(\Sigma)$ denote

$\{L \subseteq \Sigma^* : L$ *is recognisable by a* $k-tape$ *Turing machine* $\}$

Theorem 2.2: $\forall\ k \in \mathbf{N}$ and Σ: $1-tape\ (\Sigma) = k-tape\ (\Sigma)$

Proof: (Outline) We omit the detailed technical construction. Obviously $1-tape\ (\Sigma) \subseteq k-tape(\Sigma)$. To prove the reverse containment the basic method is to use a $2k$-track single-tape Turing machine, M_1, to simulate the behaviour of a k-tape Turing machine, M_k. The figure below illustrates how the k tapes of M_k are stored on the single tape of M_1. $\odot$ is a special symbol whose use is explained below. c_i^j denotes the symbol stored on the ith cell of the jth tape of M_k.

Each tape of M_k is simulated by two tracks of M_1. The track labelled *Head$_j$* records the head position on tape j, using the symbol $\odot$ (the $\emptyset$ symbol marking cells not being scanned); the other track, labelled *Tape$_j$* in the figure,

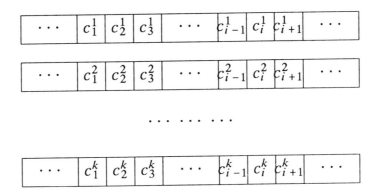

k-tape Turing machine M_k

$Head_1$	$\emptyset$	$\emptyset$	$\emptyset$	$\cdots$	$\emptyset$	$\odot$	$\emptyset$	$\cdots$
$Tape_1$	c_1^1	c_2^1	c_3^1	$\cdots$	c_{i-1}^1	c_i^1	c_{i+1}^1	$\cdots$
$Head_2$	$\emptyset$	$\odot$	$\emptyset$	$\cdots$	$\emptyset$	$\emptyset$	$\emptyset$	$\cdots$
$Tape_2$	c_1^2	c_2^2	c_3^2	$\cdots$	c_{i-1}^2	c_i^2	c_{i+1}^2	$\cdots$
$\cdots$		$\cdots$		$\cdots$		$\cdots$		$\cdots$
$Head_k$	$\emptyset$	$\emptyset$	$\odot$	$\cdots$	$\emptyset$	$\emptyset$	$\emptyset$	$\cdots$
$Tape_k$	c_1^k	c_2^k	c_3^k	$\cdots$	c_{i-1}^k	c_i^k	c_{i+1}^k	$\cdots$

(b) 1-tape Turing machine M_1

Figure 2.5: Simulation of k-tape Turing machine by 1-tape Turing machine

records the contents of the jth tape of M_k. For each move made by M_k, M_1 sweeps over the non-blank portion of its tape, recording the symbol under the marked head position for each tape. This can be done using storage in the finite control since there are only k symbols to be remembered.

The current state and these symbols are used to determine which new symbols would be printed and in what direction each of the k heads would move after application of the state transition function of M_k. In addition the next state of M_k can be found. Again, by using storage in the finite control, the k symbols to be printed and the changes of head position can be remembered and the corresponding tracks of M_1 amended to agree with the new content and head position of each tape. This sequence of operations continues for each move made by M_k. □.

Exercises

1. Construct the control graph of a Turing machine which recognises the language $EVEN \subseteq \{0, 1\}^*$ of Example 1.3.

2. Give the sequence of instantaneous descriptions for the machine of Figure 2.3 on input 00110.

3. The simulation of a k-tape Turing machine by a 1-tape Turing machine involves a great increase in the number of moves made to recognise any language. Is this actually necessary? (Hint: Consider the language over $\Sigma = \{0,1\}$ consisting of all words which are palindromes. For a given input word of length n, how many moves are made by the best 2-tape Turing machines accepting this? How many are made by the best 1-tape Turing machine accepting the same language?)

Chapter 3

Turing machines as recognisers

You may object that it is not a trial at all; you are quite right, for it is only a trial if I recognise it as such.

Franz Kafka
Der Prozess

In the previous chapter we introduced our first model of computation: the 1-tape Turing machine. A Turing machine may be viewed as a device for recognising languages: given an input word on its tape the machine performs some computation which results in it halting in the *accept* state if the input occurs in the language and halting in the *reject* state if the input does not occur in the language. Turing machines may also be regarded as mechanisms for computing arithmetic functions; without loss of generality we may restrict attention only to those functions whose domain and range are the natural numbers, **N**. When taking this viewpoint the input word supplied to the Turing machine is an encoding of the arguments to the function being computed and some interpretation of the content of the tape, after the machine halts, defines the result of the computation. The two possible approaches illustrate an important property of Turing machines: that a given Turing machine program is *both* a program which recognises some language over the tape alphabet *and* a program computing some function over the natural numbers.

One cornerstone of the study of computation is the fact that there are languages that cannot be recognised by any Turing machine program or (equivalently) there are functions over the natural numbers that cannot be correctly computed for every input by Turing machine programs. As we shall see below such results are more than mere technical limitations on the power of Turing machines as computing devices: as a consequence of accepting the Church-Turing hypothesis, languages that cannot be recognised by Turing machines cannot be recognised by *any* 'reasonable' model of computation.

In this chapter we introduce a classification of languages according to the 'extent' to which they can be recognised; we prove the *existence* of languages in each class (the question of identifying explicit languages in each category is the subject of the next chapter); various properties of each class are proved; and then, for completeness, we review the concept of Turing machines as computers of arithmetic functions; finally, we state and discuss the important Church-Turing hypothesis.

Before giving a formal description of the classification referred to in the preceding paragraph, it is useful to motivate this in less technical terms. Given a finite description of some infinite language, e.g. the set of all prime numbers, there are two types of recognition algorithm one might consider. Ideally one would seek a recognition procedure that not only came to a halt and accepted those words in the language but also halted and rejected those words not in the language. Intuitively one would regard those languages for which such recognition methods could be found as 'effectively computable' (assuming one ignores issues such as the amount of time or memory that may be required). It may happen, however, that one cannot devise a recognition algorithm that satisfies both these criteria, in which case one may be prepared to compromise with a weaker type of recognition method: one that always halts and accepts input words which are in the language *but* may fail to terminate when started with an input word that is not in the language. Intuitively these could be seen as 'partially computable' languages. The final possibility is that it is not even possible to construct a recognition algorithm that can be guaranteed to halt for inputs in the language or for inputs not in the language. Languages with this property we would consider to be 'non-computable'.

A language that can be recognised by a procedure of the first type described above is called a *recursive* language; languages that are 'partially recognised' by algorithms of the second type are called *recursively enumerable*. Formally these are defined as

Definition 3.1: Let Σ be an alphabet and $L \subseteq \Sigma^*$. The language L is said to be *recursively enumerable (r.e.)* if there exists a Turing machine program, M, such that $\forall x \in L$, M on input x eventually halts in the accept state q_A and $\forall x \notin L$, M either fails to halt or halts in the reject state q_R. We denote the class of all r.e. languages by $R.E.$ An important subset of the r.e. languages can be identified with the property that such may be recognised by some Turing machine program that always halts. Thus $L \subseteq \Sigma^*$ is said to be *recursive* if there exists a Turing machine program, M, such that $\forall x \in L$, M on input x eventually halts in the accept state q_A and $\forall x \notin L$, M on input x eventually halts in the reject state q_R.   •

The word *recursive* in the definition above is an archaic mathematical term deriving from early work on computability that predates the first modern computers. Its meaning is effectively what is understood by recursion in a Computer Science context.

Before examining the classes of r.e. and recursive languages in more depth we will digress a little to consider alternative terminology and clarify our subsequent usage. Various synonyms occur for the term *'recursive'* in the literature. The most common of these are: computable, decidable and solvable. We will use the term *decidable* when discussing *languages* (equivalently *sets*) and *computable* when concerned with functions over the natural numbers. Similarly the terms undecidable and non-computable (or uncomputable) have been used to refer to languages which are not *recursive*. Following the convention of the preceding sentence we again use *undecidable* when referring to languages and non-computable when describing functions. Note that this assumes that recursive languages are what would be regarded as corresponding to those problems solvable by 'reasonable' algorithms. Since it is sometimes useful to distinguish those languages which are r.e. but not recursive from those which are not even r.e. we will refer to the former as 'partially decidable'. The phraseologies 'having a semi-decision procedure' or 'having a quasi-decision procedure' have also been used elsewhere. Subsequently we shall use the term 'Turing machine' to be equivalent to the term 'Turing machine program'. For obvious reasons we shall adopt the term *always halting* Turing machine for one which recognises a recursive language.

At this stage a natural question to ask is why it should be thought that there are languages that are not r.e. To answer this we establish the *existence* of such entities. Later specific examples will be introduced.

The existence results are obtained through a powerful and elegant technique called *diagonalisation*. This was discovered by the great German mathematician György Cantor in the late nineteenth century. Diagonalisation provides a means of comparing the 'sizes' or *cardinalities* of two infinite sets in the following sense. Suppose Δ and Θ are two infinite sets. Even though Δ and Θ are infinite one can sensibly interpret the statement 'Δ has the same size as Θ' as meaning 'there exists a bijective mapping $\chi : \Delta \longleftrightarrow \Theta$'. That is every member of Δ can be associated with a unique member of Θ and vice versa. In this way if there is no surjective mapping from Δ to Θ, say, then the set Θ 'has more members' than Δ, or in Cantorian terminology 'the *cardinality* of Θ is greater than the cardinality of Δ'. Cantor's diagonalisation argument is a method for showing that one infinite set has greater cardinality than another by use of proof by contradiction.

The general form of the argument is as follows: consider $\mathbf{N}$, the set of natural numbers and $\mathbf{R}^+$ the set of positive reals in the open interval $(0,1)$. We wish to establish that $\mathbf{N}$ has smaller cardinality than $\mathbf{R}^+$. Suppose this is not the case, then there exists a surjective mapping $\chi : \mathbf{N} \to \mathbf{R}^+$. (Informally the mapping may be regarded as 'counting' the real numbers since it identifies a first, second, third, and so on real number). Now, because any real number may be written as a (non-terminating) decimal number, χ may be represented as an (infinite) table of the form shown in Table 3.1.

χ	1st	2nd	3rd	$\cdots$	i'th	$\cdots$
1	$.\xi_1$	a_2	a_3	$\cdots$	a_i	$\cdots$
2	$.b_1$	ξ_2	b_3	$\cdots$	b_i	$\cdots$
3	$.c_1$	c_2	ξ_3	$\cdots$	c_i	$\cdots$
$\cdots$		$\cdots$		$\cdots$	$\cdots$	$\cdots$
$\cdots$		$\cdots$		$\cdots$	$\cdots$	$\cdots$
n	$.d_1$	d_2	d_3	$\cdots$	ξ_i	$\cdots$
$\cdots$		$\cdots$		$\cdots$	$\cdots$	$\cdots$
$\cdots$		$\cdots$		$\cdots$	$\cdots$	$\cdots$

Table 3.1: Enumeration of positive reals

The leftmost column lists the natural numbers in ascending order; each row gives the decimal expansion of the positive real number to which the nth natural number is mapped by χ (each entry in a row being a single digit). Now consider the diagonal entries, which are marked out as ξ_j in the enumeration table and extend out infinitely. Consider the real number whose decimal expansion is defined by

$$\theta_j = \begin{cases} (\xi_j + 1) & if\ 0 \leq \xi_j \leq 8 \\ 1 & if\ \xi_j = 9 \end{cases}$$

By the assumption that χ exists, the real number

$$.\theta_1\,\theta_2\,\theta_3\ \cdots\ \theta_{i-1}\,\theta_i\,\theta_{i+1}\ \cdots$$

must appear somewhere in this table, in the mth row say. But from the construction θ_m differs in its mth digit from the mth column of this row. From this contradiction it follows that χ is not a surjective mapping from $\mathbf{N}$ onto $\mathbf{R}^+$ and this establishes that the positive reals have greater cardinality than the natural numbers.

We now apply this method to prove the existence of languages that are not r.e. Before proceeding with this we make the following observation about effective algorithms for Turing machines (or any other 'reasonable' model of computation): all programs are *finite*; thus any Turing machine, *M*, can be completely described by some finite word over the alphabet {0,1} e.g. one such encoding would be to use the ASCII representation of a text describing a Turing machine. A more compact encoding will be described in the next chapter. For the moment it is sufficient to observe that, using some consistent encoding, any Turing machine can be represented by a finite binary word which in turn corresponds to some natural number. It follows from this that we can sensibly use the concept of a 'first', 'second', $\cdots$, '*n*th' Turing machine merely by ordering machines according to the natural numbers by which they are encoded. We call such an ordering an *enumeration* of Turing machines. In addition we need the following definition.

Definition 3.2: The *canonical ordering* of the set of words {0,1}* is the ordering arising from the relation $\leq_{can}$ defined by the rules:

For $x \in \{0,1\}^*$ and $y \in \{0,1\}^*$, we say that $x \leq_{can} y$ if and only if

$$
\begin{cases}
x = y \\
\qquad or \\
|x| < |y| \\
\qquad or \\
|x| = |y| \ and \ x = 0.u, \ y = 1.v \\
\qquad or \\
|x| = |y| \ and \ x = \sigma.u, \ y = \sigma.v \ and \ u \leq_{can} v
\end{cases}
$$

where $\sigma \in \{0,1\}$. •

The ordering is

ϵ, 0, 1, 00, 01, 10, 11, 000, 001, 010, 011, 100, 101, . . . ,

i.e. words are ordered first by length with words of the same length ordered 'alphabetically' (using the symbol ordering $0 < 1$).

Theorem 3.1: There exist languages over $\{0,1\}^*$ that are not r.e.

Proof: Suppose the contrary, i.e. that every subset L of $\{0,1\}^*$ is an r.e. language. Let

$$TM_1, TM_2, \ldots, TM_i, \ldots ;$$

be any enumeration of Turing machine descriptions, for machines with input words over the alphabet $\{0,1\}$. Since each Turing machine accepts *some* r.e. language and every Turing machine appears in the enumeration, by the assumption that every language over $\{0,1\}^*$ is r.e., we can associate each such language with the Turing machine recognising it. (of course, some languages may be associated with more than one machine but this does not affect the argument which will rely on the assumption that *every* language has been matched with *at least one* Turing machine). Any language, L, can be described by an infinite length binary string $m_1 m_2 \cdots m_{i-1} m_i m_{i+1} \cdots$ where $w_j \in L \iff m_j = 1$, $w_j \notin L \iff m_j = 0$ and w_j is the jth word in the canonical ordering of $\{0,1\}^*$. From the preceding discussion we can construct the form depicted in Table 3.2.

In this table m_k^j denotes whether w_k is accepted by the jth Turing machine TM_j, where $m_k^j \in \{0,1\}$. Now consider the language, *DIAG*, whose defining binary string ρ is

$$\rho_j = \begin{cases} 0 & \text{if } m_j^j = 1 \\ 1 & \text{if } m_j^j = 0 \end{cases}$$

Canonical ordering of $\{0,1\}^*$

	ϵ	0	1	$\cdots$	w_k	$\cdots$
TM_1	m_1^1	m_2^1	m_3^1	$\cdots$	m_k^1	$\cdots$
TM_2	m_1^2	m_2^2	m_3^2	$\cdots$	m_k^2	$\cdots$
TM_3	m_1^3	m_2^3	m_3^3	$\cdots$	m_k^3	$\cdots$
$\cdots$		$\cdots$		$\cdots$		$\cdots$
TM_k	m_1^k	m_2^k	m_3^k	$\cdots$	m_k^k	$\cdots$
$\cdots$		$\cdots$		$\cdots$		$\cdots$

Table 3.2: Enumeration of Turing machines against languages over $\{0,1\}^*$

$DIAG \subseteq \{0,1\}^*$ and therefore, from the assumption that all languages over $\{0,1\}^*$ are r.e., there is some Turing machine accepting and halting on all words in $DIAG$. Suppose this is the kth Turing machine in the enumeration. This now yields a contradiction because if $w_k \in DIAG$ then TM_k does not halt and accept on input w_k and if, on the other hand, $w_k \notin DIAG$ then TM_k halts and accepts on input w_k. These follow since ρ, the defining binary string for $DIAG$ satisfies $\rho_k \neq m_k^k$. It follows that the string ρ corresponding to $DIAG$ cannot appear in the enumeration table and this proves that there are some languages which are not r.e. □

The next result describes some properties of r.e. languages and recursive languages.

Theorem 3.2: Let $L_1 \subseteq \{0,1\}^*$ and $L_2 \subseteq \{0,1\}^*$.

a.   If L_1 and L_2 are both r.e. then so are the languages $L_1 \cup L_2$ and $L_1 \cap L_2$.

b.   If L_1 and L_2 are both recursive then so are the languages $L_1 \cup L_2$ and $L_1 \cap L_2$.

c.   If L_1 is r.e but not recursive then the language $CO - L_1 = \{0,1\}^* - L_1$ is not r.e.

d.   If L_1 is recursive then so is the language $CO - L_1$.

Proof:

a. Since L_1 and L_2 are both r.e. there exist Turing machines M_1 and M_2 that halt and accept on exactly those words in L_1 and L_2 respectively. The language $L_1 \cap L_2$ can be recognised by a Turing machine $M_\cap$ that, given any input word $x \in \{0,1\}^*$, proceeds as follows. $M_\cap$ simulates M_1 with input x; if M_1 halts and accepts, $M_\cap$ then simulates M_2 with input x, accepting and halting if M_2 also accepts and halts. Clearly $M_\cap$ accepts and halts if and only if both M_1 and M_2 accept and halt, i.e. if and only if $x \in L_1 \cap L_2$. The language $L_1 \cup L_2$ is recognised by a Turing machine $M_\cup$ that simulates single moves of M_1 alternating with M_2 accepting if and only if one of the simulations halts and accepts.

b. The proof is similar to (a) and is left as an exercise.

c. Suppose $CO - L_1$ is r.e. Then we can construct a Turing machine recognising L_1 that always halts, i.e. we can show that L_1 is recursive, contradicting the statement of (c). To do this simply construct a Turing machine that simulates alternately one step of a Turing machine accepting L_1 followed by a step of the Turing machine recognising $CO - L_1$. If $x \in L_1$ then the first simulation eventually terminates and accepts, in which case the constructed machine terminates and accepts. Otherwise if $x \in CO - L_1$ the second simulation eventually terminates and accepts, in which case the constructed machine terminates and rejects.

d. This is trivial and left as an exercise. □

One of the consequences of part (c) of the above theorem is that we can construct languages that are not r.e. merely by identifying languages that are not recursive.

Although the concentration on decision problems as recursive or r.e. sets would be sufficiently general, it is useful to develop these ideas further to take account of computing functions over the natural numbers. The conventional method, for Turing machines, is to encode natural numbers in *unary*. Thus for any single argument function, $f: \mathbf{N} \to \mathbf{N}$, there is an equivalent function $f - unary: \{0\}^* \to \{0\}^*$. $f - unary(0^n)$ is defined to be:

$$\begin{cases} 0^m \iff f(n) = m \text{ and } f(n) \text{ is defined} \\ undefined \text{ otherwise i.e. } f(n) \text{ is not defined} \end{cases}$$

(So that the input number n is encoded as a word containing n 0s.)

Note that f may be a *partial function*, i.e. undefined for some arguments.

For k-argument functions, $f: \mathbf{N}^k \to \mathbf{N}$, the k input numbers $<n_1, n_2, \ldots, n_k>$ can be encoded as a word of the form

$$0^{n_1} 1 \, 0^{n_2} 1 \, \cdots \, 1 \, 0^{n_k}$$

(i.e. with 1s separating the unary encoding of the arguments). The equivalent unary encoding function $f - unary$ is defined in the obvious way.

We can now modify the definition of a Turing machine to express the idea of computing functions over the natural numbers.

Definition 3.3: Let $f: \mathbf{N}^k \to \mathbf{N}$ be any function over the natural numbers. f is said to be a *partial recursive function*, if there exists a Turing machine, M, that, given $0^{n_1} 1 0^{n_2} \cdots 1 0^{n_k}$ as input, halts (in either state) with the word $0^{f(n_1 \cdots n_k)}$ on the leftmost portion of its tape whenever $f(n_1 \cdots n_k)$ is defined, and fails to halt if $f(n_1 \cdots n_k)$ is not defined.

f is said to be a total recursive function, if M is a partial recursive function and is defined for all inputs $<n_1, \ldots, n_k> \in \mathbf{N}^k$. •

Intuitively the class of partial recursive functions correspond to the r.e. sets and the total recursive functions to recursive languages. The objection may be raised that this correspondence is unnatural for two reasons: the question of whether a particular word belongs to a language always has a definite answer and therefore an analogously defined function (the so-called *characteristic function*[†] is always total; and secondly we have allowed machines that accept languages that are r.e. (but not recursive) to be able to halt for some words not in the language. There are a number of ways in which we could overcome this objection, none of which is entirely satisfactory: we might define the characteristic function of a language to be undefined for inputs not contained in the language, but this has the disadvantage of not giving as simple a definition of the recursive languages; alternatively, since we consider functions whose range is $\mathbf{N}$ and have defined the output to be the number of 0s on the extreme left of the tape, we might regard an output tape that starts with the symbol *1* to constitute an undefined output.

So far we have been considering the concepts of computability (for functions) and decidability (for languages) solely with respect to single-tape Turing machines. We saw

---

[†] If L is a language over $\{0,1\}^*$ the *characteristic function*, $f_L : \{0,1\}^* \to \{0,1\}$, is defined as $f(x) = 1$ if and only if $x \in L$ and 0 otherwise. One could also define this function as having domain and range $\mathbf{N}$ by using the position of input and output words in the canonical ordering of words as the function argument.

at the end of the previous section that two possible extensions to the definition of a Turing machine (2-way infinite tape and multiple tapes) do not increase the number of computable functions or decidable languages. The contention that Turing machines compute all the functions one would intuitively regard as computable is summarised in the important

Church-Turing Hypothesis (Informal statement): A language that is partially decidable by some 'reasonable' model of computation is partially decidable by a Turing machine; a language that is decidable by some 'reasonable' model of computation is decidable by a Turing machine; a function that is computable by some 'reasonable' model of computation is computable by a Turing machine.

Church-Turing Hypothesis (First formulation): The partial recursive functions are exactly the functions that can be evaluated by any 'reasonable' computer model. •

Church-Turing Hypothesis (Second Formulation): The r.e. languages are exactly those languages for which partial decision procedures exist on 'reasonable' models of computation; the recursive languages are exactly those languages for which complete (i.e. always terminating) decision procedures exist on 'reasonable' models of computation.

Of course these contentions are unprovable, since one can never precisely define what is meant by 'reasonable'.[†] Evidence in support of the Church-Turing hypothesis comes from the fact that all mathematical models of computation that have been proposed to date can be shown to (partially) decide (r.e. and) recursive languages, and compute only partial recursive functions, i.e. all such models can be simulated

---

† The hypothesis could be *disproved* by constructing a 'reasonable' model that computed a function that was not partial recursive.

by Turing machines. This includes such diverse models as

a.   Markov algorithms.

b.   Post machines.

c. λ-Calculus.

d.   Unlimited register machines.

e.   Gödel-Kleene μ-recursive functions.

f.   Gödel-Herbrand-Kleene equational calculus.

A number of these will be encountered later in the text.

These share certain properties that we would intuitively regard as holding for any 'reasonable' computer model. We have identified one of these already: that all programs are finite. In fact a stronger property than this holds which is technically known as *uniformity*. A *uniform* model is one which, to solve a decision problem or compute a function, uses a *single finite* program to deal with *all* input sizes. It is also possible to define *non-uniform* models in which different programs are defined for different input word lengths. A second common property is that all these models provide only a finite set of operations with which to construct programs. Finally all use only finite input and output alphabets.

One advantage of accepting the Church-Turing hypothesis is that this obviates the need to give detailed machine descriptions in order to prove that specific languages are decidable or particular functions are computable: one may establish such by giving a sufficiently detailed description of an appropriate algorithm in a more intelligible formalism, such as a program in a high-level language, and then appeal to the hypothesis to exhibit computability by Turing machines; in fact any algorithmic description for which it is 'intuitively' clear that the method may be 'implemented' will suffice as a proof of computability. We shall adopt such thinking in subsequent proofs which require a device with particular computational properties to be constructed.

Exercise 3.1: Why is it necessary to alternate the simulation steps in order to recognise $L_1 \cup L_2$ in the proof of Theorem 3.2(a)?

Exercise 3.2: Show that the function $f(n,m) = n + m$ is a total recursive function. Is the function $f(n,m) = \lceil n/m \rceil$ total recursive?

Exercise 3.3: Using a diagonalisation argument, prove that there exist functions that are not partial recursive.

Exercise 3.4: Decision problems over the alphabet $\{0,1\}$ may be regarded as *Boolean functions*. Thus given $L \subseteq \{0,1\}^*$ we can define an infinite sequence of functions $f_n : \{0,1\}^n \rightarrow \{0,1\}$ by $f_n(w) = 1$ if and only if $w \in L$ (where $|w| = n$). It can be shown that any such n-input function can be expressed in terms of the Boolean operations $\wedge$ (logical AND) $\vee$ (logical inclusive-OR) and $\neg$ (logical negation). Using this property, define a model of computation that can solve *any* decision problem. Why does this *not* contradict the Church-Turing hypothesis? **Hint:** consider in what way your model of computation is 'unreasonable'.

Chapter 4

Universality

Non omnia possumus omnes

Publius Vergilius Maro
Eclogues; VIII, 63

In one sense our definition of a Turing machine, in its concentration on the concept of effective algorithm, may seem incomplete as a model of general purpose computers since it appears not to allow for the concept of *stored program.* Thus one has specific Turing machine descriptions geared to the recognition of particular r.e. languages or computation of specific partial recursive functions. In this chapter we consider *universal Turing machines.* These are Turing machines that take as input some encoding of a Turing machine, M, together with an input word, x, for it and determine (by simulation) whether $x \in L(M)$, i.e. whether M accepts x. Of course to construct such machines we need to have some standard method of encoding arbitrary Turing machine descriptions as finite strings. One approach was loosely sketched in the previous section. We now give a much more concise scheme.

The following theorem allows us to consider only encodings of machine descriptions of the form:

$$M = (Q, \{0,1\}, \{0,1,B\}, \delta, q_1, B, q_2, q_3)$$

Theorem 4.1: Let Γ be any finite alphabet and $L \subseteq \Gamma^*$ be a language recognised by a Turing machine, M_Γ, with input alphabet $\Gamma \cup B$. There is a mapping $\sigma : \Gamma^* \rightarrow \{0,1\}^*$ and a Turing machine $M_{\{0,1\}}$ such that

$$x \in L(M_\Gamma) \quad \Leftrightarrow \quad \sigma(x) \in L(M_{\{0,1\}})$$

Proof: (Outline) Let $\Gamma = <\gamma_1, \ldots, \gamma_k>$. We can construct a Turing machine $M_{\{0,1\}}$ which behaves as M_Γ by using the string 0^i to encode the symbol γ_i and separating distinct 'symbols' on its tape by the symbol 1. Thus an input

$$\gamma_{i_1} \gamma_{i_2} \cdots \gamma_{i_n}$$

for M_Γ would be represented by the input word

$$1 0^{i_1} 1 0^{i_2} 1 \cdots 1 0^{i_n} 1$$

for $M_{\{0,1,B\}}$. It is straightforward, although tedious, to construct the state transition function of $M_{\{0,1\}}$ from that of M_Γ so that the tape contents and state after k moves always correspond to the tape contents and state of the simulated machine after k moves. $\square$

The constructed universal Turing machine will also have input alphabet, $\Gamma = \{0,1,B\}$ and output alphabet $\Sigma = \{0,1\}$. In addition the initial state is always q_1, the accept state always q_2, and the reject state always q_3. With these conventions we can describe *any* Turing machine M as above, just by encoding its state transition function δ. Let us denote the symbols 0, 1, B by S_1, S_2 and S_3 respectively; and the directions *Left* and *Right* by D_1 and D_2. Then from the definition of δ, every move is of the form:

$$\delta(q_i, S_j) = (q_k, S_l, D_m) \qquad (4.1)$$

where $1 \leq i, k \leq |Q|$, $1 \leq j, l \leq 3$ and $1 \leq m \leq 2$.

Any move having the form (4.1) is encoded by a binary string

$$0^i 1 0^j 1 0^k 1 0^l 1 0^m \qquad (4.2)$$

Since δ describes a finite number of possibilities — recall that $\delta : Q \times \Gamma \to Q \times \Sigma \times \{L,R\}$ — there are at most $|\Gamma| . |Q| \leq 3|Q|$ different moves for the class of Turing machines being considered, so δ may be completely described by a finite binary word which will have the form,

$$111 \; move_1 \; 11 \; move_2 \; 11 \; \cdots \; 11 \; move_r \; 111 \qquad (4.3)$$

where each $move_i$ is a string of the form of (4.2) encoding a different move of δ. Note that the ordering of the moves is unimportant so M may have $r!$ equally valid distinct codings. We shall use the notation $\beta(M)$ to denote any valid encoding of a Turing machine M. So given a Turing machine, M, and an input word x, both of these can be represented by the binary word $\beta(M)x$. The following facts about this encoding scheme are important:

F1. Any binary string is the encoding of at most one Turing machine. This is easily seen by observing that no string of the form in (4.2) contains two adjacent 1s and hence the $code_i$ terms may be deciphered directly from (4.3).

F2. The language $TM - CODE \subset \{0,1\}^*$ defined by

$$TM - CODE = \{x : x = \beta(M) \; for \; some \; Turing \; machine \; M\}$$

is recursive.

Theorem 4.2: There exists a Turing machine, *UM*, which given an input word $u \in \{0,1\}^*$ behaves as follows:

U1. If $u = \beta(M)x$ and $\beta(M)$ is an encoding of the form (4.3) for some Turing machine M, then *UM* simulates M on input x, i.e. if M halts and accepts (rejects) x then *UM* halts and accepts (rejects) u. If M fails to halt on input x then *UM* fails to halt on u. Similarly if M computes some partial recursive function, $f - M$, then *UM* return the same result given by M on input x.

U2. If u does not encode a Turing machine and input then *UM* goes into a non-terminating loop.

Proof: Applying Theorem 2.2 on the simulation of k-tape Turing machines by 1-tape Turing machines, we construct *UM* as a 3-tape Turing machine. The first tape of *UM* holds the input, u; the second the contents of the tape of M where M is the Turing machine being simulated if $u = \beta(M)x$; the third tape contains the current state of M as it is being simulated. This current state is represented as 0^i if M is in state $q_i \in Q$.

First *UM* checks if its input u defines a valid Turing machine code $\beta(M)$ together with an input word x for M. From F2 this can be carried out. If u does not define a valid Turing machine code then *UM* goes into an infinite loop. Otherwise *UM* copies the input word x for M onto its second tape, and places 0^1 on its third tape to initiate the simulation of M with input x. The head movements on Tape 2, the current state on Tape 3 and the contents of Tape 2 can all be determined by *UM* looking up the appropriate move of δ as encoded on Tape 1 and then carrying out its effect by changing the number of 0s on Tape 3 (change of state) and the contents and head position on Tape 2. After each move of M, *UM* checks the state recorded on Tape 3;

if it is $00 \equiv q_2$ of M then UM halts and accepts; if it is $000 \equiv q_3$ of M, UM halts and rejects. Thus for decision problems, UM halts and accepts on input $\beta(M)x$ if and only if M halts and accepts on input x. So if $L(M)$ is recursive, UM on input $\beta(M)x$ always halts. If M computes a partial recursive function, the contents of Tape 2 of UM contain the same result computed by M, if the function is defined for the given input. □

Corollary 4.1: The language $L_u = \{\, \beta(M)x : x \in L(M)\,\}$ is r.e. □

However the next theorem establishes that this language is *not recursive*. The proof illustrates an important technique used in many undecidability results: that of assuming a given language is recursive and then using the properties of an always halting Turing machine recognising it to construct a contradiction.

Theorem 4.3: The language $L_u = \{\, \beta(M)x : x \in L(M)\,\}$ is not recursive.

Proof: Suppose the contrary. Then there is an always halting Turing machine, M_u say, which recognises L_u. We can use the presumed existence of M_u to construct another Turing machine, *BAD*, with the following properties: *BAD* takes as input a Turing machine code, $\beta(M)$. Now since $\beta(M) \in \{0,1\}^*$ the *code itself* may be used as an input to the machine M. Given $\beta(M)$, *BAD* proceeds to simulate the behaviour of M_u with input $\beta(M)\beta(M)$. M_u eventually halts given this input: if M_u accepts $\beta(M)\beta(M)$ (i.e. $\beta(M)\beta(M) \in L_u$) then *BAD* halts and *rejects* $\beta(M)$; on the other hand if M_u rejects $\beta(M)\beta(M)$ (i.e. $\beta(M)\beta(M) \notin L_u$) then *BAD accepts* $\beta(M)$. This behaviour is depicted in Figure 4.1 below.

Note that if *BAD* is provided with a valid Turing machine code as input then it always halts. It should be

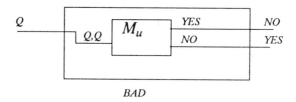

Figure 4.1: The Turing machine *BAD*

clear that if M_u exists then *BAD* does also. Now consider the behaviour of *BAD* given its *own code*, $\beta(BAD)$, as input (much as one might consider using a high-level language compiler to compile itself). First suppose that *BAD* halts and accepts; this happens only if M_u rejects $\beta(BAD)\beta(BAD)$; since M_u recognises L_u this would only happen if *BAD* did not accept $\beta(BAD)$. This is a contradiction. Thus the only possibility left is that *BAD* rejects $\beta(BAD)$. Similarly this would imply that M_u accepted $\beta(BAD)\beta(BAD)$, i.e. $\beta(BAD) \in L(BAD)$. This is again a contradiction. It follows that our initial assumption, that L_u is recursive, must be false and this completes the proof of the theorem. □

One important consequence of our encoding scheme is that it defines a mapping from the class of all Turing machines to the natural numbers (by regarding the string as the binary representation of a natural number) and hence a means of *numbering* all r.e. languages or partial recursive functions.

Unfortunately this mapping is not surjective since not every n would yield a Turing machine description. It is useful to extend this to a *bijective* mapping, $\gamma : TM - CODE \longleftrightarrow \mathbf{N}$, which is invertible; then for any $n \in \mathbf{N}$ we could designate a unique Turing machine description as the nth Turing machine. We define γ as follows.

Since Turing machine codes, as described above, may be regarded as binary representations of natural numbers, they can be ordered. In this way the 'first' Turing machine code is the one whose binary number is the lowest of all such numbers representing valid Turing machine codes. In general, $\gamma : TM - CODE \longleftrightarrow \mathbf{N}$ is given by:

a.   For a given Turing machine, M, $\gamma(\beta(M))$ is the position at which $\beta(M)$ occurs in the normal ordering of valid Turing machine codes as natural numbers. $\gamma(\beta(M))$ is called the *Gödel number* of the Turing machine, M.

b.   For any $n \in \mathbf{N}$, $\gamma^{-1}(n)$ is nth Turing machine code.

Theorem 4.4: γ and γ^{-1} are total computable functions. That is there exist Turing machines M_γ and $M_{\gamma^{-1}}$ which output the Gödel number of M given input $\beta(M)$ (output the code $\beta(M)$ given its Gödel number as input). Both machines always halt since γ is bijective (hence total over both domain and range).

Proof: To compute γ simply use a Turing machine which goes through the minimal binary representation of each n from 1, 2, 3 , . . . , counting the number of valid Turing machine codes seen until $\beta(M)$ appears. Recall from F) that the set $TM - CODE$ is recursive. To compute γ^{-1} this process is reversed: simply go through binary representations of 1, 2, $\cdots$ counting the number of valid Turing machine codes seen. The nth code (for input n) is the required Turing machine code to be output. $\square$

As we observed at the start of the preceding chapter, Turing machines can be viewed as recognising r.e. languages *and* as computing partial recursive functions. We can thus define the nth r.e. language, L_n, and the nth partial recursive function, Φ_n, as:

$$L_n = L(\gamma^{-1}(n)) \; where \; \gamma(\beta(M)) = n \qquad\qquad \text{(r.e.)}$$

$$\Phi_n = \phi : \mathbf{N} \to \mathbf{N} \qquad\qquad\qquad \text{(Function)}$$

computed by the Turing machine with Gödel number n

It should be noted that since we are numbering languages and functions via the Turing machines recognising and computing them any specific language or function will actually be counted infinitely often, since infinitely many appropriate Turing machines will exist for it.

The main reason for developing this formalism is to define a *universal language*, L_{univ}, and a *universal function*, ϕ_{univ}.

Definition 4.1: w_i is the ith word in the canonical ordering of words over $\{0,1\}$. $L_{univ} = \{0^n 1 0^m : w_m \in L_n\}$. $\phi_{univ} : \mathbf{N} \times \mathbf{N} \to \mathbf{N}$ is the (partial) function $\phi_{univ}(n,m) = \Phi_n(m)$. •

Theorem 4.5:

i. L_{univ} is r.e.

ii. ϕ_{univ} is a partial recursive function.

Proof: Use Theorem 4.4 to produce the Turing machine code $\gamma^{-1}(n)$. It should be clear, from the definition of canonical ordering, that w_m can be computed given 1^m. Thus Theorem 4.2 can be used to perform the simulation on the appropriate input word for the machine with code $\gamma^{-1}(n)$. □

We conclude this section by proving a result which will be important in the proof of Gödel's theorems in the final chapter.

Since L_n is a r.e. language over the alphabet $\{0,1\}$ it is valid to consider whether it contains the word w_n.

Suppose the following sets are defined

$$S_0 = \{w_n : w_n \notin L_n\} \; ; \; S_1 = \{w_n : w_n \in L_n\}$$

Definition 4.2: Two sets A and B over $\{0,1\}^*$ are said to be *recursively inseparable* if $A \cap B = \emptyset$ and there is no recursive set C such that $A \subseteq C$, $B \subseteq \{0,1\}^* - C$. •

Theorem 4.6: S_0 and S_1 are recursively inseparable.

Proof: Suppose not. Since $S_0 \cap S_1 = \emptyset$, by the definition of recursively inseparable, there exists some recursive language, $R \subseteq \{0,1\}^*$, such that,

R1. $S_0 \subseteq R$

R2. $S_1 \subseteq \{0,1\}^* - R$

Since R is recursive there exists an always halting Turing machine, M_R say, which recognises R. Let $\gamma(\beta(M_R)) = m$ say and consider the word w_m.

If $w_m \in S_0$ then by definition we obtain $w_m \notin L_m = R$ and hence $w_m \notin S_0$ since $S_0 \subseteq R$.

On the other hand if $w_m \in S_1$ then by definition we obtain $w_m \in L_m = R$. Now we have another contradiction since in this case it must hold that $w_m \notin S_1$, since $S_1 \cap R = \emptyset$.

In combination we have that if $w_m \in S_0$ then $w_m \notin S_0$, and if $w_m \in S_1$ then $w_m \notin S_1$. If R exists one of $w_m \in S_0$ or $w_m \in S_1$ must hold. Since neither can be true it follows that R does not exist and therefore S_0 and S_1 are recursively inseparable as claimed. □

Chapter 5

Undecidability

Of motives for some act, propose a few,
Confessing that you can't yourself decide;
Or interpose a witness to provide,
Despite his inclination to be true,
Some fadings of the signal, as it were,
A breath which, drawing closer, may obscure
Mirror or window with a token blur —
That slight uncertainty which makes us sure.

Richard Wilbur
Advice from the Muse

In the previous sections we have shown that there exist languages that are not r.e. by using a diagonalisation argument. Obviously, since the recursive languages form a subset of the r.e. sets, this result implies the existence of non-recursive languages also. Recall that Theorem 3.2(c) showed that if we have any language, L, that is r.e. but not recursive then the language $CO-L$ is not r.e. Thus to find examples of specific non r.e. languages we need only to find non-recursive sets. In this section we prove that the languages arising from some specific computational problems are not recursive. Such languages are also said to be *undecidable*.

From a Computer Science perspective, the question of whether a language is non-recursive is quite strongly motivated: even if a language is r.e. it does not imply the existence of a useful algorithm, for the recognition algorithm may fail to halt. Thus a proof that a specific language is undecidable implies that there is no effective algorithm for it. There can (at most) be a 'partial' decision process.

One problem for which it would be useful to have an algorithm is that of determining whether any program with a given input stopped or went into an infinite loop. Formally using Turing machines we can describe this as,

Definition 5.1: The *halting problem for Turing machines,* is the language $HP \subset \{0,1\}^*$ defined by,

$$HP = \{\beta(M)w : M \; halts \; on \; input \; w \} \qquad \bullet$$

Exercise 5.1: Show that HP is r.e. •

The similarility of the proof below to the proof that the language L_u of the previous chapter is not recursive should be noted.

Theorem 5.1: The halting problem for Turing machines is undecidable, i.e. the language HP is not recursive.

Proof: Suppose the contrary and that HP is recursive. Then there exists a Turing machine, M_{HP}, accepting HP that always terminates; i.e. given a Turing machine code, $\beta(M)$, and an input word w for M, M_{HP} halts and accepts if M halts on input w; M_{HP} halts and rejects if M does not halt on input w. Using M_{HP} we can construct another Turing machine, *BAD*, which behaves as follows: *BAD* takes as input a Turing machine code $\beta(M)$; *BAD* then simulates

M_{HP} on input $\beta(M)$ $\beta(M)$; if M_{HP} accepts this input then *BAD* goes into an infinite loop; if M_{HP} rejects this input, then *BAD* halts and accepts. The behaviour of this machine is depicted schematically in Figure 5.1.

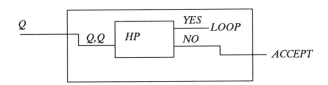

Figure 5.1: The Turing machine *BAD*

Now *BAD* is a Turing machine and hence $\beta(BAD)$ is a Turing machine code. Given this fact consider the behaviour of *BAD* on input $\beta(BAD)$. Suppose *BAD* halts and accepts. This can only happen if M_{HP} rejects the input $\beta(BAD)$ $\beta(BAD)$; that is only if *BAD* does not halt on input $\beta(BAD)$. On the other hand if *BAD* does not halt then this can only happen if M_{HP} accepts the input $\beta(BAD)$ $\beta(BAD)$; that is only if *BAD* halts on input $\beta(BAD)$. In summary *BAD* halts on input $\beta(BAD)$ if and only if *BAD* does not halt on input $\beta(BAD)$. This contradiction proves that M_{HP} does not exist and hence the language *HP* is not recursive. □

The question of whether an algorithm halts on a given input is an example of one decision problem concerned with programs. In practice one might also be interested in questions about particular languages, assuming that the set of all words in a language can be represented in a finite manner, e.g. the infinite set $\{2, 3, 5, 7, 11, 13, \ldots, \}$ can be finitely described as 'the set of all prime numbers' (assuming a definition of 'prime number'). Examples of such questions might be:

i.   Does the language contain any words at all?

ii. Is a particular word, e.g. ε, in the language?

iii. Is the language recursive?

Note that the first question *is* non-trivial, as may be seen by considering the following three languages over $\{0,1\}$:

5.1. The language *Fermat* consisting of all words of the form 1^n where $n \geq 3$ and is such that the equation $x^n + y^n = z^n$ has a solution for integer values of x, y and z.

5.2. The language *Odd −perfect* consisting of all words of the form 1^n where n is an odd perfect number i.e. a natural number which is equal to the sum of its factors excluding the number itself.

5.3. The language *Goldbach* consisting of all words of the form 1^n where n is an even number greater than 2 which *not* the sum of two prime numbers.

The question of whether any of these three languages are empty has yet to be answered: the language *Fermat* is empty if and only if Fermat's Last Theorem is true; the conjecture that all perfect numbers are even dates from Euclid's time; and the existence of even numbers, greater than 2, that are not the sum of two primes is denied by Goldbach's Conjecture.

Now, it is easy to see that all three languages are r.e. (in fact the last two are both recursive) so if there were an *always halting* Turing machine which, given a finite description of a r.e. language, could determine whether that language was empty or not, then we would be able to *mechanically* construct *mathematical proofs* of Fermat's Last Theorem, the non-existence of odd perfect numbers, and Goldbach's Conjecture, or show the existence of examples which disprove them. Both types of proof would be based on the correctness of the Turing machine program and on the sequence of moves executed given a suitable description of the relevant language.

The next two results are theorems of Rice (1953, 1956) that characterise which properties of r.e. languages are recursive and which r.e. The first of these establishes that a program with the behaviour described in the preceding paragraph does not exist.

Examples of property which might be of interest are: given a Turing machine code $\beta(M)$

i.   Is $L(M) = \emptyset$?

ii.   Is $L(M)$ recursive?

iii. Is $\epsilon \in L(M)$?

etc

Rice's Theorem for recursive index sets, which we prove next, establishes that all these languages (i.e. $\{\beta(M) : L(M)$ *has property X*$\}$) are non-recursive. In fact the only decidable properties of r.e. sets are the *trivial* ones. Before stating and proving Rice's Theorem for recursive index sets, we need to develop a more formal definition of 'property' and find some representation of the set of languages with any specific property. Recall that we deal with languages over $\{0,1\}^*$.

Definition 5.2: Let $\Pi \subseteq R.E.$, the set of r.e. languages over $\{0,1\}^*$. Π is said to be a *property* of the r.e. languages. A language L is said to *have property* Π if and only if $L \in \Pi$. •

Now suppose that for some given property Π we wish to determine if a given Turing machine, M, satisfies $L(M) \in \Pi$. Since every $L \in \Pi$ is r.e. there exists at least one Turing machine, M_L, accepting L. So the decision problem 'Is $L(M) \in \Pi$?' is equivalent to 'Does $\beta(M)$ occur in the set

$\{\beta(R) : L(R) \in \Pi\}$?'. In other words the problem of determining whether an r.e. language ($\equiv$ *Turing machine*) has property Π is equivalent to deciding membership in the language L_Π defined by

$$L_\Pi = \{\beta(M) : L(\beta(M)) \in \Pi\}$$

A property is said to be *trivial* if every r.e. language has the property ($\Pi = R.E.$) or no r.e. language has the property ($\Pi = \emptyset$). For example the property 'L is r.e.' is a trivial property since every language in *R.E.* is r.e.; the property 'L is not r.e.' is trivial since no language in *R.E.* satisfies it. Clearly the languages corresponding to trivial properties are recursive: Simply use a Turing machine which accepts any input code (if $\Pi = R.E.$) or rejects any input code (if $\Pi = \emptyset$). Rice's Theorem for recursive index sets states that these are the *only properties* Π whose associated languages, L_Π, are recursive.

Theorem 5.2: (Rice's Theorem for recursive index sets) L_Π is recursive if and only if Π is trivial.

Proof: For Π trivial we have already shown that L_Π is recursive, so it remains to establish the 'only if' assertion. That is, to show that L_Π *is recursive* $\Rightarrow$ Π *is trivial*. To do this we show that if this assertion is false then we can construct a Turing machine, M_u, which accepts $L_u = \{\beta(M)\, w : w \in L(M)\}$ and always halts. This would imply that L_u is recursive, contradicting the result of Theorem 4.3 above and therefore proving Theorem 5.2.

Suppose the contrary and that for some property Π with $\emptyset \neq \Pi \neq R.E.$, the language L_Π is recursive. From Theorem 3.2(d) the complement of a recursive language is also recursive, and so, without loss of generality, it may be assumed that $\emptyset \notin \Pi$ (otherwise we can consider the property $R.E. - \Pi$ which by the preceding remarks satisfies $L_{R.E. - \Pi}$

is recursive and $R.E. - \Pi$ is non-trivial).

Π is non-trivial so it contains some (non-empty) r.e. language, L. Since L is r.e. there exists some Turing machine, M_L which accepts L. Since we have assumed L_Π to be recursive, there exists some Turing machine, M_Π, accepting L_Π and always halting. We shall use M_L and M_Π to construct M_u.

We first construct a Turing machine, *AWKWARD*, which takes as input a Turing machine code, $\beta(M)$, and an input word w for M, and produces as output a Turing machine code $\beta(IMPOS\,(M,w))$ which satisfies

$$L(IMPOS\,(M,w)) \in \Pi \iff \beta(M)w \in L_u$$

$IMPOS\,(M,w)$ is constructed to behave as follows; we do not give a detailed Turing machine construction for *AWK-WARD* since, in view of the commentary concerning the Church-Turing hypothesis (pp. 40-41 above), the informal description below is sufficient to prove its existence. From the design of $IMPOS\,(M,w)$, *AWKWARD* may be seen as a sort of 'compiler' producing a new Turing machine, i.e. $IMPOS\,(M,w)$, using $\beta(M)$ and w.

1. $IMPOS(M,w)$ takes as input any word $x \in \{0,1\}^*$.

2. $IMPOS(M,w)$ simulates M on input w. If M halts and rejects, then $IMPOS\,(M,w)$ goes into an infinite loop.

3. If M on input w halts and accepts then $IMPOS(M,w)$ simulates M_L on the input x, accepting x if and only if M_L accepts x.

This behaviour is depicted in Figure 5.2 below.

It should be clear from this construction that $L(IMPOS\,(M,w))$ is either $\emptyset$ (if $w \notin L(M)$) or M_L (if $w \in L(M)$). Since $\emptyset \notin \Pi$ and $L \in \Pi$ we have that

$$L(IMPOS\,(M,w)) \in \Pi \iff \beta(M)w \in L_u$$

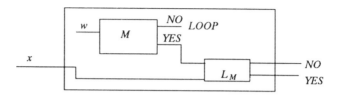

Figure 5.2: The Turing machine *IMPOS(M,w)*

By the assumption that L_Π is recursive, we can use the Turing machine M_Π to show that L_u is recursive. The Turing machine M_u accepting L_u and always halting behaves as follows. (Recall that M_u takes as input a Turing machine code $\beta(M)$ and an input word w for M.)

1. M_u simulates the Turing machine *AWKWARD* on input $\beta(M)w$. This produces the Turing machine code $\beta(IMPOS(M,w))$.

2. M_u simulates the Turing machine M_Π with input $\beta(IMPOS(M,w))$ halting and accepting if M_Π halts and accepts, halting and rejecting if M_Π halts and rejects.

The correctness of this construction for M_u is immediate from the preceding arguments. Thus L_Π *is recursive* $\Rightarrow$ L_u *is recursive* and this contradiction proves the theorem. $\square$

Theorem 5.2 considers which properties Π give rise to *recursive* languages L_Π and succeeds in finding a precise characterisation of these. The question of which properties Π yield *r.e.* languages L_Π is much more difficult. It may be noted that, in terms of the mathematical proof examples given previously, if the property of being empty were r.e. then there would still be some possibility of constructing a mechanical proof of correctness for the three open problems stated: this would be assuming that each of the conjectures were correct.

Theorem 5.3: (Rice's Theorem for r.e. index sets) L_Π is r.e if and only if Π satisfies all of the following conditions.

E1. If $L \in \Pi$ and $L \subseteq L'$ for some r.e. L' then $L' \in \Pi$.

E2. If $L \in \Pi$ and L is infinite, then some finite subset of L is in Π.

E3. The set of finite languages in Π can be *enumerated,* i.e. there is a Turing machine that generates the (possibly infinite) string $lan_1 \# lan_2 \# \cdots$, lan_i being a binary encoding of the ith finite language of Π (in any ordering). A finite language $\{w_1, \ldots, w_p\}$ is coded by just $w_1, \ldots, w_p$. •

E1 is called the *containment condition,* and states that for each $L \in \Pi$ every r.e. superset of L must also be in Π.

Note: In the following proofs we shall use the device, introduced in establishing Theorem 5.2, of employing a 'compiler' Turing machine, *AWKWARD,* which, given a Turing machine code $\beta(M)$ and a word w, generates a new Turing machine code $\beta(IMPOS(M,w))$, the properties of which will allow contradictions to be derived.

The theorem is proved with the assistance of the following lemmata.

Lemma 5.1: The language

$$CO - L_u = \{ \beta(M)w : w \notin L(M) \}$$

is not r.e.

Proof: Immediate from Theorem 3.2(c) and Theorem 4.3. □

Lemma 5.2: Let $\Pi \subseteq R.E.$ If Π does not satisfy the containment condition then L_Π is not r.e.

Proof: Suppose $L_1 \in \Pi$, $L_1 \subset L_2 \in R.E$ and $L_2 \notin \Pi$. We shall show that L_Π is not r.e. Assume the contrary and let M_1 and M_2 be Turing machines accepting L_1 and L_2 respectively. By the assumption, there exists some Turing machine, M_Π, which accepts L_Π. It will be shown that M_1, M_2 and M_Π may be used to construct a Turing machine, M_{nu}, accepting $CO - L_u$. From this we could deduce that $CO - L_u$ was r.e., contradicting Lemma 5.2.

Construct a Turing machine, $AWKWARD$, which, given $\beta(M)w$ as input, outputs a Turing machine code $\beta(IMPOS(M,w))$, $IMPOS(M,w)$ behaving as follows on input x.

1). $IMPOS(M,w)$ simulates M on input w; if $w \in L(M)$ then $IMPOS(M,w)$ simulates M_2 on input x.

2. In parallel with the simulation in (1), i.e. alternating the steps of each simulation, $IMPOS(M,w)$ simulates M_1 on input x.

3. $IMPOS(M,w)$ accepts x if either of the simulations in 1 or 2 accept x.

Thus $IMPOS(M,w)$ accepts L_1 if $w \notin L(M)$, and $L_1 \cup L_2 = L_2$ if $w \in L(M)$. (Recall that $L_1 \subset L_2$.) It follows that $L(IMPOS(M,w)) \in \Pi$ if and only if $w \notin L(M)$. Using M_Π and $AWKWARD$ we can construct M_{nu} as follows: M_{nu} simulates $AWKWARD$ on input $\beta(M)w$ to produce the code $\beta(IMPOS(M,w))$. M_{nu} then simulates M_Π on this code, accepting if and only if M_Π accepts. Now because $L_1 \in \Pi$ and $L_2 \notin \Pi$ this construction is correct. Since $CO - L_u$ is not r.e., this yields a contradiction and proves the lemma. □

Lemma 5.3: Let $\Pi \subseteq R.E.$ If Π contains an infinite language L and no finite subset of L is in Π then L_Π is not r.e.

Proof: Suppose the contrary. Again we shall construct a Turing machine, M_{nu}, which accepts $CO - L_u$. Let M_L be a

Turing machine accepting L. For this result, *AWKWARD*, on input $\beta(M)w$, produces a Turing machine code, $\beta(IMPOS(M,w))$, for a machine $IMPOS(M,w)$ such that:

1. Given an input x, $IMPOS(M,w)$ simulates M_L on input x.

2. If $x \in L(M_L)$, $IMPOS(M,w)$ then simulates M on input w for $|x|$ moves only. If $x \notin L(M_L)$ then $IMPOS(M,w)$ loops indefinitely.

3. If M has not accepted w after $|x|$ moves, then $IMPOS(M,w)$ halts and accepts x. Otherwise it enters an infinite loop.

If $w \in L(M)$ then it must be accepted after some finite number of moves, j say. It follows that $L(IMPOS(M,w))$ is L if $w \notin L(M)$ and $\{x : x \in L \text{ and } |x| < j\}$ otherwise. Now this latter is a finite subset of L and hence not in Π. It follows that

$$w \notin L(M) \iff L(IMPOS(M,w)) \in \Pi$$

So if L_Π were r.e., we could construct a Turing machine, M_{nu}, accepting $CO - L_u$, using the same arguments as Lemma 5.2 and Theorem 5.2. This proves the lemma. □

Lemma 5.4: $\mathbf{Q}^+$ is enumerable, i.e. there exists a Turing machine, $Q - GEN$, which generates all the rational numbers, in the form $0^i 10^j$ to represent i/j, each rational p/q appearing after some finite number of moves.

Proof: $Q - GEN$ simply implements the procedure below:

$$s := 2 \; ; i := 1 \; ; j := 1;$$

while true do
  output $(0^i \, 1 \, 0^j);$
  $i := i + 1 \; ; j := j - 1;$
  if $j = 0$ **then**
    $s := s + 1 \; ; j := s - 1 \; ; i := 1$
  fi
od

Thus rationals are generated in the order of increasing sum of numerator and denominator, and increasing numerator for equal sums, i.e.

$$(1,1)\,(1,2)\,(2,1)\,(1,3)\,(2,2)\,(3,1) \; \cdots \; (i,j) \; \cdots \qquad \square$$

Lemma 5.5: Let $\Pi \subseteq R.E.$ If L_Π is r.e., then the set of finite languages in Π can be enumerated in the sense of condition E3.

Proof: First observe the each finite language $\{w_1, \ldots, w_p\}$ over $\{0,1\}$ can be represented by a binary string: use 00 to encode the symbol ','; 10 to denote a 0 in a word; and 11 to denote a 1 in a word. The string 01 will be interpreted as the null symbol. The finite language enumerator, *FLE*, employs the rational generator $Q - GEN$ of the preceding lemma.

When the string $0^i \, 1 \, 0^j$ is printed *FLE* converts i to binary (adding a leading zero if the number of digits in the representation is odd) and interprets the result as describing some finite language (using the coding scheme described). *FLE* then constructs the code of a Turing machine, $M^{(i)}$, which accepts *exactly* those words in the finite language encoded by i. This can be done since all $M^{(i)}$ has to do is determine if its input matches one of a *finite* number of possibilities, halting and accepting if it does; halting and rejecting if not. Having constructed $\beta(M^{(i)})$, *FLE* then simulates M_Π, the Turing machine accepting L_Π, on input $\beta(M^{(i)})$ for exactly j moves. If $\beta(M^{(i)})$ is accepted within this many moves then *FLE* prints the code for the language (i.e. the binary representation of i) followed by a spacing symbol '#'. In either case, *FLE* returns to $Q - GEN$ to process the next generated pair in the same way. □

Proof of Theorem 5.3: The 'only if' direction has already been established by Lemmas 5.2, 5.3 and 5.5. So suppose $\Pi \subseteq R.E.$ for which conditions E1-E3 all hold. We wish to show that L_Π is r.e. We build a Turing machine, M_Π, which accepts L_Π in the following stages.

1. Let $\beta(M)$ be the input Turing machine code to M_Π. This should be accepted if and only if $L(M) \in \Pi$.

2. M_Π uses $Q - GEN$ to generate strings of the form $0^i 1 0^j$, one at a time.

3. When $0^i 1 0^j$ is generated, M_Π simulates the actions of a finite language enumerator for Π for i steps. Condition E3 shows that such an enumerator exists and so this step is valid.

4. Suppose L is the last finite language in Π completely generated by the preceding step after i moves. (If no language is completely printed then control passes to generate the next $0^i 1 0^j$). M_Π simulates M for j steps on each word in L. If M accepts every word in L then M_Π halts and accepts $\beta(M)$. Otherwise M_Π continues with the next string generated by $Q - GEN$.

We claim that M_Π, as above, accepts $\beta(M)$ if and only if $L(M) \in \Pi$. First suppose $L(M) \in \Pi$. By condition E2 some finite subset $L' \subseteq L(M)$ is also in Π. The code for the (finite) language L' must be printed by the finite language enumerator after some number of steps i. Let j be the maximum number of moves taken by M to accept any word in L'. It follows from the construction that $\beta(M)$ is accepted at Step 4 once $Q-GEN$ has generated the word $0^i 1 0^j$.

On the other hand suppose M_Π accepts $\beta(M)$. We must show that $L(M) \in \Pi$. By construction there is some (i,j) such that M accepts every word in the last language completely printed out after i steps of the enumerator, and uses at most j steps to accept any word. Since this language, L' say, is produced in Step 3, by a machine which generates only finite languages in Π, it follows that $L' \in \Pi$. But $L' \subseteq L(M)$ (since M accepts L') so from E1, the containment condition, we have $L(M) \in \Pi$ also as required. □

Corollary 5.1: The following properties of r.e. languages are not r.e.:

i. $L = \emptyset$

ii. $L = \{0,1\}^*$

iii. L is recursive.

iv. L contains exactly one word.

Proof: (i) does not satisfy E1; (ii) does not meet E2; (iii) violates E1 (Exercise: Why?); (iv) violates E1. □

Bibliography

Rice, H.G: (1953) Classes of recursively enumerable sets and their decision problems; Trans. AMS, 89, 25-59

Rice, H.G: (1956) On completely recursively enumerable sets and their key arrays; Jnl. Symbolic Logic, 21, 304-41

Chapter 6

Alternative models

Der Regel Güte daraus man erwägt,
dass sie auch 'mal 'ne Ausnahm verträgt.

Richard Wagner
Die Meistersinger von Nürnberg
Act III, Scene 5

In Chapter 2 one basic model of computation, the Turing machine, was introduced and it was shown that the precise definition chosen did not adversely affect its ability to compute those functions which would be regarded as "intuitively computable". Thus the concepts of r.e., recursive and partial recursive function could all be defined with respect to one-way infinite single-tape Turing machines. Many other models of computation have been considered. The Church-Turing hypothesis asserts that none of these are more powerful than Turing machines. In this chapter we consider a number of differing models of computation and provide some justification for this assertion by outlining how Turing machines may simulate each of them. In this way the class of recognisable languages and computable functions is not extended by any of the alternative vehicles.

6.1. Post machines

The first alternative model we consider is a string manipulation system introduced by the U.S. logician Emil Post in 1936. *Post machines* — as Turing machines — execute programs composed from a small set of basic instructions. These instructions operate on a single input word and each program consists of a finite number of labelled statements.

Definition 6.1: A *Post machine, PM, over* $\Sigma = \{0,1\}$ is a program with a single input word $x \in \{0,1,\#\}^*$, $\#$ being a special *auxiliary symbol.* The program instructions fall into the following classes:

P1. The *start* instruction, **start**, which occurs exactly once in *PM*.

P2. The *halting* instructions, **accept** and **reject**.

P3. *Test* instructions, which are of the form:

$$n: \text{ if } x = \epsilon \text{ then goto } \epsilon(n) \text{ else}$$
$$hd := head(x) ; x := tail(x);$$
$$\text{if } hd = 0 \text{ then goto } 0(n) \text{ elif}$$
$$hd = 1 \text{ then goto } 1(n) \text{ else goto } \#(n) \text{ fi}$$
$$\textbf{fi}$$

ϵ denotes the empty word and $\epsilon(n)$ etc. are numbered instructions. Test instructions will subsequently be denoted by **goto($0(n)$, $1(n)$, $\#(n)$, $\epsilon(n)$)**.

P4. *Assignment* instructions, which are of the form,

$$x \leftarrow x\theta ; \textbf{goto } (n)$$

In this instruction $\theta \in \{0,1,\#\}$ and **goto** (n), where n is some

numbered instruction, is an explicit jump.

Post machines are simple programs utilising a small set of instructions to manipulate words. A word, $x \in \{0,1\}^*$ is said to be *accepted* (*rejected*) by the Post machine, *PM*, if *PM* when started with input x eventually reaches an **accept** (**reject**) instruction.   •

As with Turing machines, we can define the language recognised by a Post machine, $L(PM)$, and further subdivide such languages into those that can be accepted by Post machines which always halt, and those that are accepted by Post machines which may fail to halt on some words not in the language.   For languages over $\{0,1\}$ we let *Post −rec* denote the former class and *Post −enum* the latter.

Theorem 6.1: $\forall \ \ L \ \subseteq \{0,1\}^*$

i. $L \in Post-enum \quad \Longleftrightarrow \quad L \in R.E.$

ii. $L \in Post-rec \quad \Longleftrightarrow \quad L$ is recursive.

Proof: The $\Rightarrow$ directions are relatively straightforward; i.e. informally anything solvable by a Post machine is solvable by a Turing machine. Since the number of instructions is finite each of these can correspond to several states of a Turing machine, M. Initially, M holds the input word x on its tape and its initial state corresponds to the unique **start** instruction of the Post machine, *PM*. The operations of appending a new symbol can be easily simulated by shifting the current word one place right and adding the appropriate new symbol (so one step of *PM* may require several moves of M to be made, hence several states are needed for a single instruction). Note that we can use a two-way infinite tape to avoid the problem of moving too far left in searching for the start of the word. The only other action is that of testing the first symbol and deleting it. Here a special blank marker Δ can be used and the symbol read stored in finite control to move to the start of the next instruction.

The $\Leftarrow$ direction is a little more complicated and we will merely outline the construction. To simulate a Turing machine, M, a Post machine is constructed whose input word, x, at each stage of the simulation will encode the contents of the Turing machine tape together with the current head position. Suppose that

$$ID_t \;=\; c_1 c_2 \;\cdots\; c_{k-1} q_i c_k \;\cdots\; c_m B$$

is the instantaneous description of M on its input after t moves have been executed. Then the corresponding word stored in x for the simulating Post machine will be

$$x \;=\; c_k \;\cdots\; c_m \,\#\, c_1 c_2 \;\cdots\; c_{k-1}$$

Note that the blank symbol is ignored and that the symbol scanned by the Turing machine tape head is the leftmost symbol in x. In addition the contents of M's tape have been rotated with the $\#$ symbol used to mark the rightmost non-blank symbol.

The relevant state transition executed by M will be of the form $\delta(q_i, c_k) = (q_j, \alpha, D)$. If $D = R$ then a subprogram is invoked to change x to the form

$$c_{k+1} \;\cdots\; c_m \,\#\, c_1 c_2 \;\cdots\; \alpha$$

(which just involves appending α to end of x). If $D = L$ then x must be rotated until it is of the form

$$x \;=\; c_{k-1} \alpha c_{k+1} \;\cdots\; c_m \,\#\, c_1 \;\cdots\; c_{k-2}$$

The only problems arise with the special cases when M's tape head moves to scan a blank symbol and when the tape head is instructed to move too far to the left. In the first

case x must be configured as $B \# c_1 c_2 .... c_{k-1} \alpha$. In the
second case (when x would have been $c_1 \cdot \cdot \cdot c_m \#$) the
Post machine program can be configured to enter an infinite loop. □

Example 6.1: The following Post machine accepts the
language $\{0^n 1^n : n \geq 0\}$

```
1:   start
2:      x ← x # ; goto  3
3:      goto( 4 , 9 , 10 , 9 )
4:      goto( 5 , 6 , 9 , 9 )
5:      x ← x 0 ; goto  4
6:      goto( 9 , 7 , 8 , 9 )
7:      x ← x 1 ; goto  6
8:      x ← x # ; goto  3
9:      reject
10:     accept
```

6.2. Unlimited register machines

These were first considered by Shepherdson and Sturgis
(1963), and are somewhat closer in spirit to Von Neumann
machines.

Definition 6.2: An *unlimited register machine,* (URM) consists
of an infinite number of *registers,* denoted
$R_1, R_2 , \ldots , R_i , \ldots ,$ each of which can hold any
whole number. r_n denotes the number held in the nth register.

Register	R_1	R_2	R_3	..	R_{i-1}	R_i	R_{i+1}	$\cdots$
Contents	r_1	r_2	r_3	..	r_{i-1}	r_i	r_{i+1}	$\cdots$

Figure 6.1: Unlimited register machine

Register contents are changed under control of a finite

program that comprises four instruction types.

URM1. $Z(n)$: This sets the contents of register R_n to the value 0 (*zero* instruction).

URM2. $S(n)$: This increments the contents of R_n by 1 (*successor* instruction).

URM3. T: This assigns, to register R_n, the value stored in register R_m (*transfer* instruction).

URM4. $J(m,n,q)$: This executes the conditional instruction 'if $r_n = r_m$ **then** **goto** q' (*jump* instruction), where q is a numbered program instruction. Operation ceases when an instruction to **goto** q where $q >$ *Number of instructions* occurs. •

Unlimited register machines are one mechanism for computing functions over **N**. The initial configuration consists of the first k registers (for some finite value k) containing the input data (i.e. function arguments) with the remaining registers holding the value zero.

Detailed technical simulations of unlimited register machines by Turing machines are fairly involved. By using the following Turing machine variation, which is a natural extension of the multitrack Turing machine, such a simulation can be made relatively easily.

Definition 6.3: A *2-dimensional Turing machine,* is one whose tape consists of an infinite (in both x and y directions) 2-dimensional grid. The directions in which the head can move are *Left* ($\equiv -1$ in x "coordinate"); *Right* ($\equiv +1$ in x coordinate); *Up* ($\equiv +1$ in y coordinate); and *Down* ($\equiv -1$ in y coordinate). •

Theorem 6.2: A single-tape Turing machine can simulate a 2-dimensional Turing machine.

Proof: Let 2D be a 2-dimensional Turing machine.   We

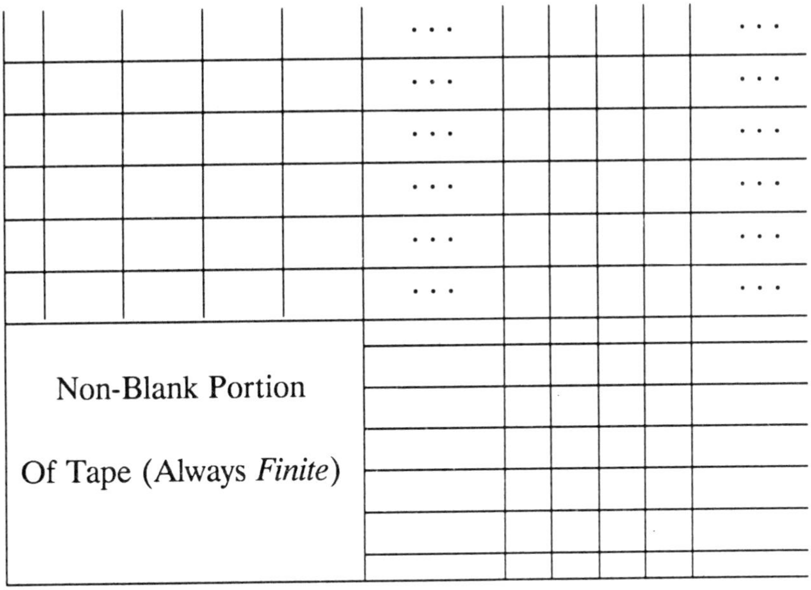

Figure 6.2: Tape of 2-dimensional Turing machine

employ a two-tape Turing machine, M, with alphabet $\{0, 1, \#\}$ to simulate this. The $\#$ symbol is used as a marker. At each stage the lower tape of M contains the non-blank portion of the tape of $2D$. This is laid out in rows separated by the $\#$ symbol so that each block of symbols between two $\#$ symbols corresponds exactly to the symbols on a unique row of the tape of $2D$. The upper tape of M contains a two-part counter which is always of the form $1^{row} \# 1^{col}$. The first block of 1s encodes the y coordinate of the tape head on $2D$; the second block encodes the x coordinate. When simulating a move of $2D$, both tape heads of M are assumed to be at the leftmost end of their respective tapes. M first uses the counter on the upper tape to access the tape cell within a row corresponding to the cell scanned by $2D$. The changes made by $2D$ are then imitated (this may involve shifting blocks of symbols on M's lower tape). The final stage is to update the counter on the upper tape to correspond with the head movement made by $2D$ and to return M's tape heads to their starting position. □

Exercise 6.1: Using the result of the previous theorem, show that Turing machines can simulate unlimited register machines. •

6.3. Markov algorithms

Markov algorithms are formal symbol manipulation systems based on *production* (or *rewrite*) rules.

Definition 6.4: A *Markov algorithm (MA)* over the alphabet $A_k = \{a_1, a_2, \ldots, a_k\}$ is a (finite) ordered sequence of *productions*. Productions have one of two forms:

$$p_j \rightarrow q_j \qquad \text{(Simple)}$$

$$p_j \rightarrow_t q_j \qquad \text{(Terminal)}$$

Let **M** be a Markov algorithm over A_k and $x, y \in A_k^*$. **M** is said to *transform* x *into* y, written **M** : $x \rightarrow y$, if p_i is the first occurrence of the left-hand side of some production occurring in x and y results from replacing the leftmost subword p_i in x by q_i. If $p_i \rightarrow_t q_i$ then **M** is said to transform x directly into y *terminally*. In the obvious way one can also define **M** *derives* y *from* x (terminally) (written **M** : $x \Rightarrow y$ (**M** : $x \Rightarrow_t y$)) if some finite sequence of productions transforms x into y. Finally we write $\mathbf{M}(x) = y$ if either **M** : $x \Rightarrow_t y$ or **M** : $x \Rightarrow y$ and no production rule can be applied to y. •

Clearly, Markov algorithms may be viewed as schemes for computing functions over **N**. The following result is easy to prove and is left as an exercise.

Theorem 6.3: $f : \mathbf{N} \rightarrow \mathbf{N}$ is a partial recursive function if and only if it is computable by a Markov algorithm. □

6.4. Turing machine variants

Previously, when we considered extensions to the Turing machine formalism described in Definition 2.1, the modifications examined only concerned the mechanisms for storing data: thus two-way infinite tape, multiple tape and two-dimensional tape Turing machines have been shown to be no more powerful than the first model defined. In this section, instead of extending the memory capabilities of a Turing machine, we consider various changes that can be made to the *state transition function*. Recall that this function is a mapping

$$\delta : Q \times \Gamma \quad \rightarrow \quad Q \times \Sigma \times \{L, R\}$$

This describes a *deterministic* machine: given a machine definition and an input for it, the behaviour of the machine on the given input can be *predicted* in advance without executing the program specified. Thus for each state and tape symbol there is exactly one move possible. An important different model is the *non-deterministic Turing machine* (NDTM).

Definition 6.5: A *non-deterministic Turing machine, M,* is defined exactly as in Definition 2.1 except that the state transition function δ is given by:

$$\delta : Q \times \Gamma \rightarrow \text{Subsets of } Q \times \Sigma \times \{L,R\}$$

This is interpreted as giving a *choice* of possible moves. An input $x \in \{0,1\}^*$ is accepted by M if *some sequence* of valid move choices leads to an accepting state. The concept of an input being rejected is not defined. In fact it may be shown that it suffices to provide only *two* choices rather than arbitrary subsets of possible moves and we will assume that this simplification has been made subsequently.

Theorem 6.4: $L \subseteq \{0,1\}^*$ is accepted by a non-deterministic

Turing machine if and only if L is r.e.

Proof: If L is r.e. then a non-deterministic Turing machine recognising L can be built from a deterministic Turing machine, M, recognising L as follows. Suppose Q is the set of states of M. Let NM be the non-deterministic machine with state set $Q \cup R$ where $|Q| = |R|$. For each move $\delta(q_i, \alpha) = (q_j, \beta, D)$ of M, NM will have moves

$$\delta(q_i, \alpha) = \{(q_j, \beta, D), (r_j, \beta, D)\}$$

$$\delta(r_i, \alpha) = \{(q_j, \beta, D), (r_j, \beta, D)\}$$

It is easy to see that if M accepts x then NM has an accepting computation path for x also.

Now suppose that $L \subseteq \{0, 1\}^*$ is accepted by some non-deterministic Turing machine NM. We can build a deterministic Turing machine M that behaves as depicted in Program 6.1.

```
Current  IDs  :=  {q₀x}
loop
    Next  IDs  :=  ∅
    for each S ∈ Current  IDs do
        Next  IDs  :=  Next  IDs  ∪   the two IDs
                    reachable from S
    od
    Current  IDs  :=  Next  IDs
    if qₐ is a state in Current  IDs then
        halt and accept
    fi
end loop
```

Program 6.1: Simulation of non-deterministic Turing machine

If NM accepts x then eventually an accepting configuration will appear in the 'current instantaneous description' set being maintained by M and so M will also halt and accept x. □

In practice all existing computers are deterministic machines: the sequence of actions executed by a given program on a given input is predictable. To this extent deterministic Turing machines capture the essential features of practical computer architectures. On the other hand the behaviour of non-deterministic Turing machines cannot be exactly reproduced by any existing sequential computer: non-deterministic algorithms cannot be implemented. This is not, however, due to the fact that the behaviour of such algorithms is unpredictable but rather because of the way in which acceptance by such algorithms is defined: *there exists some sequence of valid move choices* terminating in an accept state, i.e in terms of decision problems involving searching for an object (e.g. particular sub-graph in an input graph) a non-deterministic algorithm always "guesses correctly" if the object exists.

We now turn to a class of algorithms whose behaviour is a compromise between the two extremes of deterministically implementable and non-deterministic but unrealisable: the class of randomised or *probabilistic algorithms*.

A probabilistic algorithm is one that uses random elements in deciding what sequence of moves to make. One may view such algorithms as containing instructions which choose between two alternative actions by tossing a (possibly biased) coin and selecting one of these if the outcome is *heads* $\equiv 1$ and the other if the outcome is *tails* $\equiv 0$. Clearly the behaviour of a probabilistic algorithm is non-deterministic in the sense that the sequence of actions executed on a specific input is not predictable. However, *pace* the philosophical question of whether true random behaviour is possible, one can envisage actually "implementing" such algorithms by, ideally, employing statistically good random number generators or, at worst, by physically tossing a coin for each random choice. This motivates the question: can probabilistic algorithms be better than deterministic algorithms?

Of course phrased in this way the question is imprecisely formulated. What is meant by "better"? How do we define the output of a probabilistic algorithm? Do we allow the results returned by such algorithms to be incorrect and if so what degree of error is tolerable? In order to address these questions we must define a formal model of probabilistic computation.

Shannon *et al.* (1956) and Santos (1969, 1971) describe probabilistic models related to Turing machines. The definition below is derived from Gill (1977).

Definition 6.6: A *probabilistic Turing machine* (*PTM*), M, is a Turing machine as in Definition 2.1 but with the difference that for each $q \in Q$ and $\sigma \in \Gamma$, $\delta(q, \sigma) = (\mu_0, \mu_1)$ where

$$\mu_0, \mu_1 \ \in \ Q \times \Sigma \times \{L, R\}$$

In state q scanning σ, M randomly selects an element of $r \in \{0, 1\}$ and carries out the move corresponding to μ_r. For each q and σ $Prob\,[r = 0] = Prob\,[r = 1] = 0.5$ and these probabilities are independent of any previous choices made. •

Now suppose that M is a PTM. How are we to define $L(M)$, the set of input strings accepted by M? Since one of our aims is to view PTMs as a means of recognising specific languages, L, it is desirable that any PTM which is defined as accepting L should have a "reasonably high" probability of behaving correctly on each $x \in \{0, 1\}^*$.

Definition 6.7: Let M be a PTM. $L(M)$, the language recognised by M, is

$$L(M) = \{x \in \{0,1\}^* : P[M \, accepts \, x] > 0.5\}$$

A PTM, M, is *always halting* if and only if for all $x \in \{0,1\}^*$

$$P[M \, accepts \, x] > 0.5 \quad or \quad P[M \, rejects \, x] > 0.5$$

(N.B. This is *not* equivalent to stating that M is *certain* to halt. There may be computation paths which never terminate.)

A language $L \subseteq \{0,1\}^*$ is said to be *randomly r.e. (r.r.e.)* if and only if there exists a PTM M such that $L(M) = L$. L is *randomly recursive (r.r.)* if and only if there exists an always halting PTM, M, such that $L(M) = L$.

Following Gill (1977) we define the (random) partial function over $\{0,1\}^*$ f_M, computed by a PTM, M, as

$$f_M(n) = \begin{cases} y & if \; P[M \, halts \, with \, output \, y] > 0.5 \\ undefined & if \; there \; is \; no \; such \; y \end{cases}$$

We can thus define the class of randomly computable partial (total) recursive functions as those partial (total) functions which are computable by PTMs. Note that as with deterministic Turing machines the classes of r.r.e. and r.r. languages may be regarded as special instances of randomly computable functions.   •

It is important to note that PTMs can make errors. Thus a given M may accept some $x \notin L(M)$ since the probability of this event may be > 0; similarly M can reject some $x \in L(M)$ if $P[M \, accepts \, x] < 1$.

Our first result deals with the class of r.r.e. and r.e. languages.

Theorem 6.5: Let $L \subseteq \{0,1\}^*$.

a. L is r.r.e. $\iff$ *L is r.e.*

b. L is r.r. $\iff$ *L is recursive*

Proof: Both $\Leftarrow$ implications are immediate since Turing machines are just a restricted type of PTM in which the two possible moves for each state and input tuple are identical. So it suffices to prove $\Rightarrow$ for both cases.

To prove (a) let $L \subseteq \{0,1\}^*$ that is r.r.e. and M be a PTM such that $L(M) = L$. We will construct a deterministic Turing machine, M' for which $L(M') = L(M) = L$. We record the configuration of M during any stage of its computation on input x by an instantaneous description (*ID*). For any given *ID* of M let ID_r denote the new *ID* that results when $r \in \{0,1\}$ is selected on a move. It is convenient to define $ID_0 = ID_1 = ID$ when *ID* is a halting configuration. In addition let ID_x denote the initial *ID* when M is started with input x and define the predicate *accept* on *ID*'s to be true if and only if the current state in an *ID* is q_A.

Given M and an input x for M we can construct a Turing machine, M', that performs the actions in Program 6.2.

The probability of accepting, at each stage, can be computed since the probability of reaching a given *ID* from ID_x is just $2^{-distance(ID_x, ID)}$ where $distance(ID_x, ID)$ is the number of moves made to reach *ID* from ID_x. Now suppose $x \in L(M) = L$. Then by definition $P[M \text{ accepts } x] > 0.5$ and thus $x \in L(M')$ since M' merely generates all possible computation paths of M on x and halts and accepts only if the probability of reaching q_A exceeds 0.5. It follows that $L \subseteq L(M')$. On the other hand

Current_ID_Set := {*ID$_x$*}
Next_ID_Set := ∅
probability_of_accepting := 0
while *probability_of_accepting* ≤ 0.5 **do**
    for each *ID* ∈ *Current_ID_Set* **do**
      Next_ID_Set := *Next_ID_Set* ∪ {*ID$_0$*, *ID$_1$*}
    od
    Current_ID_Set := *Next_ID_Set*
    Next_ID_Set := ∅
    probability_of_accepting :=
$$\sum_{ID \in Current\_ID\_Set \,:\, accept(ID)} P[ID \text{ reached from } ID_x]$$
od
Halt and accept x

Program 6.2: Simulation of probabilistic Turing machine

suppose that $x \in L(M')$. This can only happen if $P[\,M \text{ accepts } x\,] > 0.5$ i.e $x \in L(M)$. This establishes that $L(M') = L(M) = L$ and hence L is r.e.

(b) is proved using a similar fashion, except that at each iteration the probability that q_R has been reached is also calculated and the termination condition tests if the probability of reaching q_A exceeds 0.5 or the probability of reaching q_R exceeds 0.5. □

An identical argument serves to show that f is randomly partial (total) recursive if and only if f is partial (total) recursive.

Theorem 6.5 establishes that in one sense *PTMs* are no more powerful than ordinary Turing machines since exactly the same class of languages can be recognised by both models.

Santos (1969, 1971) studies a form of PTM in which

arbitrary probabilities may be used in selecting moves. Thus a PTM *with bias p* (or p $-PTM$) is one in which for each $\delta(q, \sigma) = (\mu_0, \mu_1)$ we have

$$P[\mu_0 \text{ chosen}] = p \quad ; \quad P[\mu_1 \text{ chosen}] = 1-p$$

For $p \in [0, 1)$ define $R.E.(p)$ to be the class of languages $L \subseteq \{0,1\}^*$ such that L is accepted by some p-PTM. Similarly define $R(p)$ to be the class of languages accepted by some always halting p-PTM.

Definition 6.8: Let $q \in [0, 1)$ and $.q_1 q_2 \cdots q_n \cdots$ be the binary expansion of q, so that $q = \sum_{i=1}^{\infty} q_i 2^{-i}$. q is a *computable real number* if the language $L^{(q)} = \{ 1^n : q_n = 1 \}$ is recursive. Otherwise q is a non-computable real number. •

It should be clear from the results of Chapter 5 that there exist non-computable real numbers.

Theorem 6.6: If p is a computable real number then

$$R.E.(p) = R.E.(0.5) \quad ; \quad R(p) = R(0.5)$$

Proof: We prove the first relation only since the second may be shown in an identical manner. That $R.E.(0.5) \subseteq R.E.(p)$ follows from the facts that $R.E.(0.5)$ is equal to the class of r.e languages and any r.e language is obviously in $R.E.(p)$. Suppose $L \in R.E.(p)$ and M is a p-PTM accepting L. We can construct a 0.5-PTM (i.e. PTM), M' that also accepts L as follows. On input x, M' simulates M on input x but for each move $\delta(q, \sigma) = (\mu_0, \mu_1)$ of M, M' executes the procedure of Program 6.3.

Clearly

$$P[\mu_0 \text{ chosen}] = p \quad ; \quad P[\mu_1 \text{ chosen}] = 1-p$$

$i := 0$
repeat
    $i := i + 1$
    Compute bit p_i of the binary expansion of p
    Pick $r \in \{0, 1\}$ $(P[r=0] = P[r=1] = 0.5)$
until r p_i
if $r < p_i$ **then** μ_0 **else** μ_1

Program 6.3: Simulation of p-PTM

and the probability of looping indefinitely is 0. □

Corollary 6.2: If p is a computable real number then $L \in R.E. (p)$ if and only if L is r.e.; $L \in R(p)$ if and only if L is recursive.

Proof: Combination of Theorem 6.5 and Theorem 6.6. □

In contrast, however, we have a theorem originally proved in Shannon *et al.* (1956) and restated in Santos (1971). This theorem shows that some non-recursive languages belong to $R(p)$ for appropriate choices of p. The proof of this result, given below, differs from these papers.

Theorem 6.7: $\forall\ p \in [0, 1)$ the language $L^{(p)}$, corresponding to the real number p is in $R(p)$.

Proof: Let $g : \mathbf{N} \to \mathbf{N}$ be some total, computable function to be fixed subsequently. Consider the p-PTM which acts as in Program 6.4 on input 1^n (where $n \geq 1$)

Now in $g(n)$ iterations the *expected value* of l is $pg(n)$. Let $\epsilon_n = 2^{-n-1}$ and

$$u = \lceil pg(n) + \epsilon_n g(n) \rceil$$
$$d = \lfloor pg(n) - \epsilon_n g(n) \rfloor$$

If $d < l < u$ then

$$\left| \frac{l}{g(n)} 2^n - p\,2^n \right| < 1/2$$

$l := 0$

for $g(n)$ iterations **do**

    Pick $r \in \{0,1\}$ $(P[r=0] = p, P[r=1] = 1-p)$

    if $r = 0$ **then**

        $l := l + 1$

    fi

od

$par := (\ \lfloor \dfrac{l}{g(n)} 2^n \rfloor\ ) \bmod 2$

if $par = 1$ **then** *accept* **else** *reject*

Program 6.4

i.e. $l/g(n)$ and p agree in the first n bits of their binary expansion. It follows that it is sufficient to prove that for some choice of g we have:

$$P[d < l < u] \quad > \quad 1/2$$

in order to establish that the procedure above gives rise to an always halting p-PTM which accepts $L^{(p)}$.

$$P[d < l < u] = 1 - \sum_{i=0}^{d} B(i, g(n), p) - \sum_{i=u}^{g(n)} B(i, g(n), p)$$

where

$$B(i, n, p) = \begin{cases} \binom{n}{i} p^i (1-p)^{n-i} & \text{if } i \leq n \\ 0 & \text{if } i > n \end{cases}$$

From Chernoff's bound (Chernoff (1952) see Erdös and Spencer (1974), p.17):

$\forall\ \beta, p \in [0, 1]$

$$\sum_{k=0}^{\lfloor (1-\beta)np \rfloor} B(n, k, p) \quad < \quad \exp\left(\dfrac{-\beta^2 np}{2} \right)$$

$$\sum_{k = \lceil (1+\beta)np \rceil}^{n} B(n, k, p) < \exp\left(\frac{-\beta^2 np}{3}\right)$$

Therefore, with $\beta = \epsilon_n/p$

$$P[d < l < u] > 1 - \exp\left(\frac{-\epsilon_n^2 g(n)p}{2p^2}\right) - \exp\left(\frac{-\epsilon_n^2 g(n)p}{3p^2}\right)$$

$$> 1 - \exp\left(\frac{-g(n)}{2^{2n+3}p}\right) - \exp\left(\frac{-g(n)}{3.2^{2n+2}p}\right)$$

Hence since $p \leq 1$ if we fix $g(n) = 4^{n+3}$ then

$$P[d < l < u] > 1 - \exp(-8) - \exp(-16/3) > 0.5$$

Thus $L^p \in R(p)$. □

So if we consider the real number *HALT* the ith digit of whose binary expansion is 1 if and only if the ith Turing machine program halts on input ϵ, then $L^{(HALT)}$ is undecidable. Theorem 6.7, however, shows that $L^{(HALT)}$ is accepted by an always halting *PTM* with bias *HALT*. Of course this result does not contradict the Church-Turing hypothesis, since the concept of a random choice biased by an uncomputable real weight is not a 'reasonable' one.

Bibliography

Chernoff, H: (1952) A measure of asymptotic efficiency for tests of a hypothesis based on the sum of observations; Ann. Math. Stats., 23, 493-509

Erdös, P; Spencer, J: (1974) *Probabilistic methods in combinatorics*; Academic Press

Gill, J: (1977) Computational complexity of probabilistic Turing machines; SIAM Jnl. Comput., 6, 675-695

Santos, E.S: (1969) Probabilistic Turing machines and

computability; Proc. Amer. Math. Soc., 22, 704-710

Santos, E.S: (1971) Computability by probabilistic Turing machines; Trans. Amer. Math. Soc., 159, 165-184

Shannon, C.E; de Leeuw, K; Moore, E; Shapiro, N: (1956) Computability by probabilistic machines; Automata Studies, Ann. of Math. Studies, 34, 183-212

Shepherdson, H.C.; Sturgis, H.E: (1963) Computability of recursive functions; Jnl. of the A.C.M., 10, 217-55

Chapter 7

Post´s Correspondence Problem

So far only "machine based" decision problems have been shown to be undecidable, for example the halting problem and questions relating to properties of r.e. sets. In this section we introduce a problem concerned with string matching systems, known as Post's Correspondence Problem, and prove this to be undecidable.

Definition 7.1: A *Post system* S over an alphabet Σ consists of a set of $k \geq 1$ ordered pairs of words over Σ, i.e.

$$S = \{(\alpha_1, \beta_1), (\alpha_2, \beta_2), \ldots, (\alpha_k, \beta_k)\}$$

A *solution* to a Post system consists of a (non-empty) sequence of integers $i_1, i_2, \ldots, i_m$ where $1 \leq i_j \leq k$ such that

$$\alpha_{i_1} \alpha_{i_2} \cdots \alpha_{i_m} = \beta_{i_1} \beta_{i_2} \cdots \beta_{i_m}$$

This word, formed by concatenating the α_{i_j} strings, is called the *correspondence word* of a solution to the Post system. The *Correspondence Problem for Post systems, PCP,* is the decision problem of determining whether a given Post system over $\Sigma = \{0,1\}$ has a solution. •

Informally we can think of Post's Correspondence Problem in the following way: one is given an infinite deck of cards. There is only a finite number (k say) of different cards in this deck, each of which is divided into two parts. The upper half of a card has written on it some word u_i and the lower half some word l_i (for i between 1 and k). The problem is to choose a finite number of cards so that when these are placed side by side, the word formed along the upper halves is identical to the word formed along the lower halves.

Theorem 7.1: The Correspondence Problem for Post systems is undecidable.

Proof: We assume a modified class of Post machines in which the **test** instructions lead to a final state if the tested word is empty, i.e. $x = \epsilon$. It is easy to show that the halting problem for Post machines is undecidable. We shall show that any algorithm solving PCP can be used to construct an algorithm solving the halting problem of Post machines. To do this we give a uniform method of transforming a Post machine, M, and input x for M into a Post system, $S(M,x)$, such that $S(M,x)$ has a solution if and only if M halts on input x.

Suppose M is any Post machine over alphabet $\{0,1,\#\}$ and that x is an input word for M. Let M have m **test** and **assignment** instructions labelled $B_1, \ldots, B_m$ and a **start** instruction B_0, and let B_{m+1} denote any *accept* or *reject* instruction. Suppose also that $x = \theta_1 \cdots \theta_n \in \{0,1,\#\}^n$. The Post system is constructed over the alphabet $\Lambda = \{0,1,\#,*, B_0, \ldots, B_{m+1}\}$ where $*$ is an auxiliary symbol. The system $S(M,x)$ contains the following correspondences;

C1. $(B_0 ; B_0 * \theta_1 * \cdots \theta_n * B_1 *)$

C2. $(*B_i * 0 ; B_j *)$ for each **test** instruction, B_i, of the form **goto** $(B_j ; B_k ; B_l ; B_{m+1})$.

C3. $(*B_i * 1 ; B_k *)$ for each **test** instruction, B_i, of the form **goto** $(B_j ; B_k ; B_l ; B_{m+1})$.

C4. $(*B_i * \# ; B_l *)$ for each **test** instruction, B_i, of the form **goto** $(B_j ; B_k ; B_l ; B_{m+1})$.

C5. $(*B_i * B_{m+1} ; B_{m+1})$ for each **test** instruction, B_i, of the form **goto** $(B_j ; B_k ; B_l ; B_{m+1})$.

C6. $(*B_i ; \theta * B_j *)$ for each **assignment** instruction of the form $x \leftarrow x\theta$; **goto** B_j.

C7. $(*\theta ; \theta *)$ for each $\theta \in \{0,1,\#\}$.

We claim that $S(M,x)$ has a solution if and only if M halts on input x.

First suppose that $S(M,x)$ does have a solution. We wish to show that in this case the Post machine, M, halts when started with input x. Let γ be the correspondence word for this solution. Let

$$B_{i_1} ; B_{i_2} ; \cdots ; B_{i_p}$$

be the ordered sequence of instruction instances that occur in γ. Clearly $B_{i_1} \equiv B_0$ and $B_{i_p} \equiv B_{m+1}$ for otherwise it is easy to see that γ could not be a correspondence word. It follows that it is sufficient to prove that for each j $(1 \le j \le p)$ B_{i_j} is the jth instruction executed by the Post machine M on input x. This will be proved by induction on j.

The inductive base, $j = 1$, follows from the observation made earlier that $B_{i_1} \equiv B_0$ — the **start** instruction. So suppose the assertion holds for all values less than j. Let L_k and R_k denote the subwords of γ arising after the first k correspondences have been applied: thus, in terms of Definition 7.1, L_k is the result of concatenating k α words and R_k the result of concatenating the corresponding k β words. Consider the value k such that the symbol instance $B_{i_{j-1}}$ occurs in one of L_k, R_k but does not occur in either L_{k-1} or R_{k-1}. Then it must be the case that

$$ L_k \;=\; \lambda \quad ; \quad R_k \;=\; \lambda * \mu B_{i_{j-1}} * $$

where $\lambda \in \Lambda^*$ and μ is either the empty word or of the form $\mu_1 * \mu_2 * \cdots \mu_r *$ with $\mu_t \in \{0,1,\#\}$ for each $1 \le t \le r$. Now if μ is not the empty word then the next r correspondences applied must be repeated applications of C7 so that

$$ L_{k+r} \;=\; \lambda * \mu_1 * \cdots * \mu_r $$
$$ R_{k+r} \;=\; \lambda * \mu B_{i_{j-1}} * \mu $$

In order for γ to be a correspondence word, the next correspondence invoked must append $*B_{i_{j-1}}$ to L_{k+r}. From the construction of C1 through C7 this can only happen by invoking the correspondence pair that matches the form of the instruction instance $B_{i_{j-1}}$. This will result in the instruction instance which would be executed following execution of $B_{i_{j-1}}$ being appended to R_{k+r}. Since this is the instruction instance following $B_{i_{j-1}}$ in γ (i.e. B_{i_j}) and, by induction, $B_{i_{j-1}}$ is the operation carried out at time $j-1$ when M runs on x it follows that B_{i_j} is the instruction performed at time j when M runs on x. This complete the inductive proof.

The argument above establishes the first part of the theorem since the last instruction instance in the correspondence word is a halting instruction.

It remains to prove the reverse implication: if the Post

machine M halts on input x then the Post system $S(M,x)$ has a solution.

Suppose M halts on x. Let

$$B_{i_1} ; B_{i_2} ; \cdots ; B_{i_p}$$

be the sequence of instruction instances executed, so that $B_{i_1} = B_0$ and $B_{i_p} = B_{m+1}$. We prove by induction on j ($2 \leq j \leq p$) that a sequence of k_j correspondences ($k_j > k_{j-1}$) can be chosen so that

$$L_{k_j} = \lambda \quad ; \quad R_{k_j} = \lambda * \mu B_{i_j} *$$
$$or$$
$$L_{k_j} = R_{k_j}$$

where μ is as defined in the first half of the theorem proof.

The inductive base $j = 2$ follows by invoking the correspondence pair C1. For then

$$L_1 = B_0$$
$$R_1 = B_0 * \theta_1 * \cdots * \theta_n * B_1 *$$

Assume the assertion holds for all values $\leq j - 1$ so that

$$L_{k_{j-1}} = \lambda$$
$$R_{k_{j-1}} = \lambda * \mu B_{i_{j-1}} *$$

If $\mu = \epsilon$ and $B_{i_{j-1}}$ is a **test** instruction then applying correspondence C5 gives

$$L_{k_j} = \lambda * B_{i_{j-1}} * B_{m+1} = R_{k+j}$$

completing the proof. If $\mu = \epsilon$ and $B_{i_{j-1}}$ is an **assignment** instruction, then applying the relevant correspondence C6 gives

$$L_{k_j} = \lambda * B_{i_{j-1}}$$
$$R_{k_j} = \lambda * B_{i_{j-1}} * \theta * B_{i_j} *$$

which establishes the inductive step for this case.

We are left with the case where μ is not the empty word. By repeatedly applying C7 (r times say) eventually it happens that

$$L_{k_{j-1}+r} \; = \; \lambda * \mu_1 * \cdots * \mu_r$$
$$R_{k_{j-1}+r} \; = \; \lambda * \mu B_{i_{j-1}} * \mu$$

If $B_{i_{j-1}}$ is a **test** instruction then applying the appropriate correspondence pair from C2 to C4 gives

$$L_{k_j} \; = \; \lambda * \mu * B_{i_{j-1}} * \mu_1$$
$$R_{k_j} \; = \; \lambda * \mu * B_{i_{j-1}} * \mu_1 * \cdots * \mu_r * B_{i_j} *$$

which proves the inductive step for this case.

If $B_{i_{j-1}}$ is an **assignment** instruction then using the relevant C6 correspondence yields the final case.

This complete the inductive proof. The second half of the theorem now follows: since M halts on x an instruction of the form B_{m+1} must be executed. The first case analysed above ($\mu = \epsilon$ and $B_{i_{j-1}}$ is a **test** instruction) leads to a solution of the Post system $S(M,x)$. $\square$

The undecidability of Post's Correspondence Problem is useful in establishing that several apparently unrelated decision problems are also unsolvable. In this section we describe one such application to a problem concerning products of matrices.

Definition 7.2: Let $M = \{M_1, M_2, \ldots, M_r\}$ be a finite (non-empty) set of 3×3 integer valued matrices. The *(i,j)-mortality problem for M* (where $1 \leq i, j \leq 3$) is to determine if there exists a finite sequence

$$<i_1, i_2, \ldots, i_p> \in \{1,2, \ldots, r\}^p$$

such that the (i,j) entry of the 3×3 matrix

$$M_{i_1} \times M_{i_2} \times \ \cdots \ \times M_{i_p}$$

is 0. If such a product exists then M is said to be *mortal* with respect to (i,j). •

The following theorem is due to Floyd.

Theorem 7.2: The (3,2)-mortality problem is undecidable.

Proof: We shall show that given a Post system, S, over alphabet Σ a set of 3×3 matrices may be constructed which is mortal with respect to (3,2) if and only if S has a solution. Since the construction will be uniform, the existence of an algorithm for the (3,2)-mortality problem would yield an algorithm for Post's Correspondence Problem and this would contradict the result of Theorem 7.1.

Let Σ be any finite alphabet. The method used is to define a mapping $M : \Sigma^* \times \Sigma^* \rightarrow 3 \times 3$ *matrices* such that for any words $x, y \in \Sigma^*$, the matrix $M(x, y)$ satisfies:

M1. The (3,2)-entry of $M(x, y)$ is 0 if and only if $x = y$.

M2. $\forall \ x_1, x_2, y_1, y_2 \in \Sigma^*$,

$$M(x_1, y_1) \times M(x_2, y_2) \ = \ M(x_1 x_2, y_1 y_2)$$

To define this mapping we use the following functions from words over Σ to integers:

F1. $c(x) = i - 1$ when x is the ith word in the canonical ordering of words over Σ. Thus $c(x)$ is the number of words that *precede* x in the canonical ordering of Σ^*.

F2. $e(x) = |\Sigma|^{|x|}$. That is $e(x)$ is the total number of words in Σ^* with length equal to the length of x.

Lemma 7.1:

$$c(xy) \ = \ c(x)e(y) + c(y) \tag{i}$$

$$e(xy) \ = \ e(x)e(y) \tag{ii}$$

Proof: The second relation is obvious from the definition of e. For the first observe that the set of words preceding xy in the canonical ordering of Σ^* may be divided into 3 disjoint sets:

$$\Psi_1 \;=\; \{\, zw : z <_{can} x \text{ and } |w| = |y| \,\}$$

$$\Psi_2 \;=\; \{\, w : |w| < |y| \,\}$$

$$\Psi_3 \;=\; \{\, xw : |w| = |y| \text{ and } w <_{can} y\,)\,\}$$

Obviously $|\Psi_1| = c(x)e(y)$ and it is easy to see that the total number of words in $\Psi_2 \cup \Psi_3$ is exactly $c(y)$. □

For $x, y \in \Sigma^*$, the 3×3 matrix, $M(x, y)$ is defined by,

$$M(x, y) \;=\; \begin{bmatrix} e(x) & e(y) - e(x) & 0 \\ 0 & e(y) & 0 \\ c(x) & c(y) - c(x) & 1 \end{bmatrix}$$

With this definition, it is clear that the $(3,2)$ entry is 0 if and only if $c(y) = c(x)$ i.e. $x = y$. It follows that condition M1 holds. Also given x, y, v, w in Σ^*,

$$M(x, v) \times M(y, w) =$$

$$= \begin{bmatrix} e(x) & e(v) - e(x) & 0 \\ 0 & e(v) & 0 \\ c(x) & c(v) - c(x) & 1 \end{bmatrix} \times \begin{bmatrix} e(y) & e(w) - e(y) & 0 \\ 0 & e(w) & 0 \\ c(y) & c(w) - c(y) & 1 \end{bmatrix}$$

$$= \begin{bmatrix} e(x)e(y) & e(v)e(w) - e(x)e(y) & 0 \\ 0 & e(v)e(w) & 0 \\ c(x)e(y) + c(y) & (c(v)e(w) + c(w)) - (c(x)e(y) + c(y)) & 1 \end{bmatrix}$$

$$= \begin{bmatrix} e(xy) & e(vw)-e(xy) & 0 \\ 0 & e(vw) & 0 \\ c(xy) & c(vw)-c(xy) & 1 \end{bmatrix}$$

$$= M(xy, vw)$$

Establishing that condition M2 holds also.

From the preceding analysis, given an algorithm for the (3,2)-mortality problem, we can construct an algorithm for Post's Correspondence Problem.

Let $S = \{(\alpha_1, \beta_1), \ldots, (\alpha_q, \beta_q)\}$ be a Post system over Σ. Form the set of q 3×3 matrices

$$\{ M_i(\alpha_i, \beta_i) : 1 \leq i \leq q \}$$

From the definition of M it is immediate that this system is mortal with respect to (3,2) if and only if S has a solution. □

Exercise: A variant of the mortality problem is: given a finite set of 3×3 integer matrices with integer values is there a finite product of these whose result is the zero matrix. Show that this problem is undecidable.[†]

---

† A solution to this exercise may be found in:

Paterson, M.S. (1970): Unsolvability in 3×3 matrices; Stud. Appl. Math., 49 (1), 105-107

Chapter 8

Recursive Function Theory

8.1. Introduction

There is an alternative approach to the classification of computable functions which, in contrast to our previous models, is not machine based. The formalism developed by Gödel and Kleene, prior to the work of Turing, set out to capture the concept of computability by considering the classes of functions over N that result from a set of basic functions and functional composition operators. In this chapter we review the ideas underlying this approach — known as *Recursive Function Theory* — and prove some important theorems concerning Gödel numberings of recursive functions.

Let F_k denote the set of all functions $f : N^k \rightarrow N$. We use $\mathbf{x} = (x_1, \ldots, x_k)$ to denote the formal arguments of $f \in F_k$. Recall that $f(\mathbf{x})$ is a *total* function if $f(\alpha)$ is defined for all $\alpha \in \mathbf{N}^k$ and is a *partial* function otherwise.

In Chapter 3 we introduced the concepts of partial and total recursive functions. P will denote the set of all partial recursive functions and $T \subset P$ the set of all total recursive functions. Earlier we defined these classes in terms of Turing machine computation.

8.2.   Sets of functions obtainable by closure operations

Consider the following three *basic* functions

B1. The *zero* function $\mathbf{0} \in F_0$ defined as $\mathbf{0} = 0$.

B2. The *successor* function $succ(x) \in F_1$ defined as $succ(x) = x + 1$.

B3. The *projection* function $U_i^k \in F_k$ $(1 \le i \le k)$ defined by $U_i^k(\mathbf{x}) = x_i$.

Intuitively all of these functions are 'computable'. Below we introduce two methods of constructing new 'computable' functions: the techniques of *substitution* and *recursion*.

Definition 8.1: Let $f \in F_n$ and $g_1, g_2, \ldots, g_n$ be functions in F_k The function $h \in F_k$ is obtained by *substitution* from f and $g_1, \ldots, g_n$ if and only if

$$h(\mathbf{x}) \;=\; f(\, g_1(\mathbf{x}), \ldots, g_n(\mathbf{x}) \,)$$

Substitution corresponds to the process of functional composition.   •

The following is obvious:

Lemma 8.1: Let h be obtained by substitution from f and $g_1, \ldots, g_n$. h is total if $f, g_1, \ldots, g_n$ are all total. Furthermore if f and $g_1, \ldots, g_n$ are partial recursive functions, then h is a partial recursive function.   □

Definition 8.2: Let $f \in F_k$ and $g \in F_{k+2}$. The function $h \in F_{k+1}$ is obtained from f and g by *recursion* if h satisfies the *recursion equations*,

$$h(\mathbf{x}, 0) \;=\; f(\mathbf{x}) \tag{R1}$$

$$h(\mathbf{x}, y+1) \;=\; g(\mathbf{x}, y, h(\mathbf{x}, y)) \tag{R2}$$

R1 specifies the recursive base, R2 the recursive definition of h in terms of a "smaller instance" of h. •

Lemma 8.2: If h is obtained from f and g by recursion then h is total if f and g are total; furthermore if f and g are partial recursive then h is partial recursive. □

The operations of substitution and recursion provide a means of constructing an infinite class of functions from the basic functions introduced at the opening of this section.

Definition 8.3: Let Q be any class of functions. Q is said to be *closed under the operation* Ψ, if any function h, obtained from functions in Q by Ψ, satisfies $h \in Q$. Q is the *smallest* class closed under Ψ, if no proper subset of Q is closed under Ψ. •

Definition 8.4: The set of *primitive recursive functions, PR*, is the smallest class of functions containing **0**, *succ* and U_i^k ($\forall \, k \geq 1$) and that is closed under substitution and recursion. •

Note that any primitive recursive function is total recursive; the functions **0**, *succ* and U_i^k are all effectively computable and any $f \in PR$ is built from a finite number of substitution and recursion applications using these. *PR* however does not encapsulate *all* total recursive functions.

Theorem 8.1: There are total recursive functions which are not primitive recursive. □

The proof of this is somewhat involved and is omitted. Nevertheless a large number of important functions are primitive recursive.

Example 8.1: The functions *ADD*, *MULT* and *POWER* in F_2 defined by:

$ADD(x, y) = x + y.$

$MULT(x, y) = x * y.$

$POWER(x, y) = x^y.$

are all primitive recursive functions.

Proof: For *ADD* use the recursion equations $f(x) = U_1^1(x)$ and $g(x, y, z) = succ(U_3^3(x, y, z))$. Hence

$ADD(x, 0) = x \quad ; \quad ADD(x, y + 1) = succ(ADD(x,y))$

For *MULT* the recursion equations are $f(x) = 0$ and $g(x, y, z) = ADD(U_1^3(x,y,z), U_3^3(x,y,z))$ so that

$MULT(x, 0) = 0 \quad ; \quad MULT(x, y + 1) = x + MULT(x, y)$

Note that in this case we use the already established fact that *ADD* is primitive recursive. Similarly for *POWER* we have the recursion equations $f(x) = succ(0)$ and $g(x, y, z) = MULT(U_1^3(x,y,z), U_3^3(x,y,z))$ so that

$POWER(x, 0) = 1 \; ; \; POWER(x, y + 1) = x * POWER(x, y)$

Note that we have chosen to given a full formal definition of *g* in each case, in terms of the composition of some primitive recursive function and a projection function. We could equally express each *g* as $succ(z)$; $ADD(x, z)$; and $MULT(x, z)$ for the functions *ADD*, *MULT* and *POWER* respectively. □

Exercise 8.1: Give recursion equations for the *predecessor* function $pred \in F_1$, which is defined as $pred(0) = 0$ and $pred(x) = x - 1$ if $x > 0$. Using the fact the *pred* is a primitive recursive function show that the binary operator $\dot{-}$ (read *monus*) defined by $x \dot{-} y = 0$ if $x \le y$ and $x - y$ if $x > y$ is a primitive recursive function. •

Exercise 8.2: Prove that the function $ITER_k \in F_k$ defined by

$$ITER_k (x_1, \ldots, x_k) \ = \ x_1^{x_2^{\cdot^{\cdot^{x_k}}}}$$

is primitive recursive for all fixed k. Is the function $SUPER \in F_2$ where

$$SUPER(x, n) \ \equiv \ ITER_n(x, x, \ldots, x)$$

primitive recursive? •

To cover all the intuitively computable functions, i.e. the class of partial recursive functions, it is necessary to introduce another constructor operation, that of *minimalisation*. Unlike the operations of recursion and substitution this may not always yield a total function.

Minimalisation arises from attempts to define the function $g(\mathbf{x}) \in F_k$ which for any given $f(\mathbf{x},y) \in F_{k+1}$ is

$$g(\mathbf{x}) \ = \ Least \ y \ such \ that \ f(\mathbf{x},y) = 0$$

We wish to define g in such a way that g is partial recursive if f is. However the definition above may not yield this; e.g. suppose $f(\mathbf{x},0)$ is undefined, but $f(\mathbf{x},1) = 0$; even if f is computable this does not imply the minimalisation template above is. To counteract this a special minimalisation operator, μ, is used:

Definition 8.5: Let $f(\mathbf{x},y) \in F_{k+1}$. The function $g(\mathbf{x})$ is obtained by *minimalisation* from $f(\mathbf{x},y)$ if

$$g(\mathbf{x}) \ = \ \mu y.(f(\mathbf{x},y) = 0)$$

where $\mu y.(f(\mathbf{x},y) = 0)$ is the least y such that $f(\mathbf{x},z)$ is defined for all $z \leq y$ and $f(\mathbf{x},y) = 0$. The function is undefined if no such y exists. $\mu y.(\cdots)$ is read "the least y such that $\cdots$" and is called the μ-*operator*. •

Example 8.2:

i. $\mu y.\,(ADD\,(x,y)=0)$ is the function **0** if $x=0$ and is undefined for all other values of x.

ii. $\mu y.\,(MULT\,(x,y)=0)$ is the function **0** for all values of x.

iii. $\mu y.\,(POWER\,(x,y)=0)$ is undefined for all values of x.

iv. $\mu y.\,(pred\,(y)=0)$ is **0**.

v. $\mu y.\,(x \ominus y = 0)$ is the function $U_1^1(x)$ i.e. x. •

Lemma 8.3: If $f\,(\mathbf{x},y)$ is partial recursive then so is $g\,(\mathbf{x}) = \mu y.\,(f\,(\mathbf{x},y) = 0)$. □

Definition 8.6: The set of μ-recursive functions $\mu - R$ is the smallest class of functions that contains **0**, *succ* and U_i^k ($\forall\ k \geq 1$) and which is closed under substitution, recursion and minimalisation. •

Theorem 8.2: A function is partial recursive if and only if it is μ-recursive.

Proof: (Outline) If f is μ-recursive then by definition it is also partial recursive. If f is partial recursive then there is a Turing machine, M, computing f. It is a straightforward (but tedious) exercise to show that the permitted Turing machine operations on an input word may all be expressed as μ-recursive functions. Thus in composition (by virtue of closure) a Turing machine computation corresponds to some μ-recursive function definition. □

8.3. Enumerations of computable functions

In Chapter 4 we showed that a total computable function, $\gamma : TM - CODE \longleftrightarrow \mathbf{N}$, which mapped between Turing machine codes and $\mathbf{N}$ could be defined. There were two consequences of this mapping

1.   We could enumerate the partial recursive functions i.e. with each $n \in \mathbf{N}$ one could associate a specific partial

recursive function ϕ_n, namely the function computed by the Turing machine with code $\gamma^{-1}(n)$.

2. There is a *universal* partial recursive function $\Phi \in F_2$ defined by $\Phi(n, m) = \phi_n(m)$.

In this section we prove some general results on such methods of indexing the partial recursive functions. These hold for any Gödelisation of the computable functions. For example, using the result of Theorem 8.2 we can express any partial recursive function in terms of a finite number of applications of substitution, recursion and minimalisation to the three kinds of basic functions. Therefore, by suitably encoding the way in which these are applied, a different enumeration of the partial recursive functions results. The results proved below, although expressed in terms of Turing machines where appropriate, can be proved for any computable function indexing system.

The first result — the $s-m-n$ *theorem* — gives an interesting property of binary computable functions and will be useful in establishing further theorems.

Theorem 8.3: (Simple form of s-m-n theorem) Let $<\phi_i>$ be a Gödelisation of the partial recursive functions in F_1 and let $\psi \in F_2$ be a partial recursive function. There is a total computable function, $s \in F_1$ (depending on ψ) such that

$$\psi(m, n) \;=\; \phi_{s(n)}(m) \qquad \forall\; n \in \mathbf{N}$$

Proof: Let M be a Turing machine that computes ψ. Define $s \in F_1$ to be the function computed by the Turing machine, S, defined by the behaviour below:

1. S takes an input of the form 0^n.

2. S computes and outputs $0^{s(n)}$ where $s(n)$ is the Gödel number of the Turing machine S_n acting as follows.

    2.1. S_n takes an input of the form 0^m.

2.2. S_n writes the string 10^l to the right of its input returning the tape head to the first cell.

2.3. S_n simulates M on the input $0^n 10^l$ that is now written on the tape.

Clearly the machine S_n in the above construction computes $\psi(m, n)$. Since S_n has Gödel number $s(n)$ it follows that $\psi(m, n) = \phi_{s(n)}(m)$. It is clear from the construction that s is a total computable function. □.

It is straightforward to generalise the simple form of the $s-m-n$ theorem to the following.

Theorem 8.4: (General form of s-m-n theorem) Let $\mathbf{x} = <x_1, \ldots, x_k>$ and $\mathbf{y} = <y_1, \ldots, y_l>$. For $j \geq 1$ let $<\phi_i^j>$ be a Gödelisation of the partial recursive functions in F_j. For all $k, l \geq 1$ there is a total computable function in F_{k+1}, $s_k^l(n, \mathbf{x})$ such that

$$\phi_n^{(k+l)}(\mathbf{x}, \mathbf{y}) = \phi_{s_k^l(n, \mathbf{x})}(\mathbf{y}) \qquad \square$$

Informally the general form states that if we have fixed some subset, $\mathbf{x}$, of the arguments to a partial recursive function ϕ in F_{k+l} then we can compute the index of the induced partial recursive function in F_l using the index of ϕ and $\mathbf{x}$.

An interesting application of the $s-m-n$ theorem is the following.

Theorem 8.4: (Recursion Theorem) Let $<\phi_i>$ be as in Theorem 8.3. For any total computable function $f \in F_1$ there exists $k \in \mathbf{N}$ such that

$$\phi_{f(k)}(y) = \phi_k(y) \qquad \forall y \in \mathbf{N}$$

Proof: Consider the function

$$\psi(n, y) = \Phi(f(\phi_n(n)), y) \in F_2$$

(which is undefined if $\phi_n(n)$ is undefined) where Φ is the universal function. From Theorem 8.3 there is a total computable function $s \in F_1$ such that

$$\psi(n, y) \;=\; \Phi(f(\phi_n(n)), y) \;=\; \phi_{s(n)}(y) \tag{8.1}$$

Let m be the index of any Turing machine that computes $s(n)$. By rewriting (8.1) we obtain

$$\phi_{f(\phi_n(n))}(y) \;=\; \phi_{\phi_m(n)}(y) \tag{8.2}$$

If we now fix $n = m$ and write $k = \phi_m(m)$ — note the latter assignment is valid since by construction ϕ_m is a total function — then we obtain from (8.2)

$$\phi_{f(k)}(y) \;=\; \phi_k(y) \qquad\qquad \square$$

We conclude this chapter by giving some applications of the Recursion Theorem. The first looks superficially similar to the simple form of the $s-m-n$ theorem.

Corollary 8.1: Let $f \in F_2$ be a partial recursive function. There exists $n \in \mathbf{N}$ such that $\phi_n(y) = f(n, y)$ for all $y \in \mathbf{N}$.

Proof: From Theorem 8.2 there is a total recursive function $s \in F_1$ for which $\phi_{s(m)}(y) = f(m, y)$. Applying the Recursion Theorem using s we can identify an index n such that

$$\phi_n(y) \;=\; \phi_{s(n)}(y) \;=\; f(n, y) \qquad\qquad \square$$

So, for example, there are indices n such that

1. $\phi_n(m) = m^n$ for all $m \in \mathbf{N}$ (choose $f(n, m) = m^n$).

2. $\phi_n(m) = n$. This is a so-called *self-replicating* program, since it outputs its own index for all inputs.

Finally the Recursion Theorem permits a much simpler proof of Rice's Theorem for recursive index sets that was presented in Chapter 5.

Corollary 8.2: (Rice's Theorem for recursive index sets) Let

$\emptyset \subset \Pi \subset F_1 \cap T$ and define $L_\Pi = \{1^n : \phi_n \in \Pi\}$. Then L_Π is not recursive.

Proof: Suppose, for some Π, that L_Π is recursive. Let $1^n \in L_\Pi$ and $1^m \notin L_\Pi$. Define the function $f_\Pi(x)$ to be n if $1^x \notin L_\Pi$ and m if $1^x \in L_\Pi$. Then by the assumption that L_Π is recursive it follows that f_Π is a total recursive function in F_1. From the Recursion Theorem there is an index t such that $\phi_t = \phi_{f_\Pi(t)}$. Now suppose that $1^t \in L_\Pi$. Then $1^{f_\Pi(t)} \in L_\Pi$ by virtue of the fact that ϕ_t and $\phi_{f_\Pi(t)}$ are identical. This yields a contradiction since $f_\Pi(t) = m$ and by the construction $1^m \notin L_\Pi$. In the same way if $1^t \notin L_\Pi$ then $1^{f_\Pi(t)} \notin L_\Pi$ also and again a contradiction results from the facts that $f_\Pi(t) = n$ and $1^n \in L_\Pi$. In summary: either both ϕ_t and $\phi_{f_\Pi(t)}$ are functions in Π or neither of them are. The preceding arguments show that $\phi_t \in \Pi \iff \phi_{f_\Pi(t)} \notin \Pi$. This contradiction establishes the result. □

Chapter 9

Formal models of arithmetic

Reason ser's nae end but pleasure,
Truth's no' an end but a means
To a wider knowledge o' life
And a keener interest in't.

Hugh MacDiarmid
A Drunk Man Looks at the Thistle

The remaining sections of this book are concerned with the development of a precise formulation of the concept of mathematical proof, culminating with the presentation of Gödel's results on completeness and consistency in formal theories. These establish the existence, in any sufficiently powerful theory, of mathematical statements that are (self-evidently) 'true' but cannot be *proved* to be so. It may appear that this has little to do with the issues of computability with which the text has been concerned so far. However the work of Gödel on the expressive power of mathematical theories is motivated by a *computational* problem proposed by the German mathematician David Hilbert almost 90 years ago. This, the *Entscheidungsproblem*[†] may be informally stated as follows:

> Design an algorithm (program) that given a formal representation of a mathematical assertion determines whether the assertion is true (i.e. a *theorem*) or false (i.e. *logically invalid*).

If such a program exists then in a strong sense all of mathematics is trivial; since any conjecture can be validated or repudiated simply by expressing it sufficiently formally and then *mechanically* constructing a proof. Additionally such a program establishes that all mathematical reasoning is based on a secure logical foundation: all true assertions are provably so (by the correctness of the program); all false statements are provably so; and every assertion is either true or false. Attempting to establish the latter consequence occupied many mathematicians in the early 20th century. Consider the process of constructing a mathematical proof of some statement: the argument is presented as a sequence of assertions that hold given that some initial premise holds; the proof terminates with an assertion equivalent to the statement whose proof is sought. Of course the sequence of assertions used must follow some logical pattern; each should be a consequence of the preceding assertion. Underlying any mathematical theory there must be a set of *inference rules* and *axioms* that effectively allow further valid statements to be generated from any given valid statement. It is important to observe that the 'truth' of each axiom is assumed *a priori*. As we shall see below, this *axiomatic* approach leads naturally to an

---

† Literally 'The decision problem', use of a definite article being justified by this being a 'universal decision problem'.

interpretation of 'theorems' (i.e. provably true assertions) as being the set of statements that can be generated from the axioms. In this way producing a 'proof' is a particular type of rewriting (or production) system, i.e. a string manipulation process. The important consequence of this is that Hilbert's program can be written if one can find a set of axioms that

P1. Are sufficiently powerful to allow any true statement to be *proved* true.

P2. Do not admit of contradictions, i.e. either an assertion or its negation can be proved true but not *both*.

Before considering the subsequent technical development of work on the *Entscheidungsproblem* it may be helpful to attempt to understand the historical context in which the question was posed.

That a challenge such as the one set by Hilbert arose indicated a sense of unease about the basis upon which mathematical results had been constructed. In what way were such results 'true' in an absolute sense? How could one know that contradictory results could not be proved? Could every proposition be eventually verified or invalidated given sufficiently powerful tools? The first question represents the fundamental concern in the field of Philosophy of Mathematics.[†] and this and similar questions preoccupied mathematicians in the latter part of the 19th and early years of the 20th centuries.

Yet such questions would have seemed strange to the

---

† See for example Wittgenstein's *Bemerkungen uber die grundlagen der mathematik*, (Transl. as *Remarks on the foundations of mathematics;* (3rd edition), Blackwell, Oxford, 1978) or Russell's *Introduction to mathematical philosophy*, (Allen and Unwin, 1956) for illustrations of the problems that a detailed interpretation of even 'simple' constructs leads to.

generations preceding Hilbert and his contemporaries; why should they have become an issue at the end of the 19th century?

One can identify (at least) three important developments in 19th century mathematics that answer this question.

1.   Non-Euclidean geometries.

2.   The importation of logic as a mathematical tool.

3.   Cantor's work on set theory and cardinality.

Let us examine each of these briefly.

1. One of the most thorough and comprehensive examples of the process of deducing logical consequences (theorems) from a fixed set of assumptions (axioms) is contained in a collection of results compiled almost 2000 years ago: Euclid's *The Elements*. Starting from a basis of five 'obvious' propositions this proceeds, over seven books, to derive results on the properties of geometrical objects. Euclid believed that his fifth axiom, the so-called parallel postulate,[†] was redundant, i.e. it could be derived using the other four axioms. Euclid and his successors were unable to prove this. Then in the mid-19th century a number of people considered the effect of modifying the parallel postulate[‡] (in order to derive a proof by contradiction). It was discovered that each of the modified systems gave rise to valid, non-contradictory results, and that that just as classical (Euclidean) geometry could be viewed constructively as reasoning about the properties of 'real' objects, so these new (non-Euclidean) geometries had corresponding constructive

---

† This asserts that: given any line, L, and a point p not on L there is exactly one line M that contains p and is parallel to L.

‡ By assuming that zero, a fixed number greater than one, or infinitely many appropriate lines existed.

interpretations.

The discovery of non-Euclidean geometry created a difficulty: if a mathematical topic as apparently so firmly grounded in reality as Euclidean geometry can result in equally valid models simply by changing one of its basic assumptions how could one be certain that applying the same process to a more abstract area, such as the Theory of Arithmetic, would not have the same effect?

2. Despite the now widespread use of deductive logic, propositional and predicate calculus as an underlying rigorous framework in areas as diverse as pure mathematics, formal verification of programs, design of automated theorem proving systems in A.I, and the analysis of Boolean functions, it is only in the last 100 years that logic has come to be accepted as a powerful *mathematical* reasoning tool. Prior to this the Theory of Logic had advanced little since its exposition by Aristotle and it had largely been employed only in supporting the reasoning producing technical philosophical models. It was the German mathematician Frege and the Italian Peano who saw in formal symbolic logic and the, then new, concepts of set theory, a possible foundation for rigorous proofs, in particular a secure basis for the Theory of Arithmetic. However there is one deep problem in using a formal symbolic logic to represent propositions: the existence of *paradoxes*. Any assertion encoded as a proposition in symbolic logic ought to be capable of being resolved as either *True* or *False*. But one may construct propositions asserting **THIS STATEMENT IS FALSE** that have no obvious resolution.[†]

---

† Frege argued that such propositions are meaningless and therefore have a truth-value of *False*; but similar difficulties arise in trying to apply this convention consistently.

The freedom to construct paradoxes suggests that even a low-level, precise system based on symbolic logic is an inherently unsound mechanism for encoding assertions. We would expect any syntactically correct program to have a clearly defined, deterministic behaviour. Analogously the least that one would demand of a formal logical system is that any syntactically valid construct, i.e. proposition, has a definite resolution to *True* or *False* but should not be meaningless.[†]

3. Some of Cantor's work on comparing the cardinalities of infinite sets has been encountered earlier in this book. In Cantor's time the concept of what constitutes a 'set' was not clearly defined.[‡] This vagueness led to the discovery of a paradox in set theory. Cantor had proved that there was no 'largest' set: given any set S, finite or infinite, the set of all subsets of S, $P(S)$, can be shown using diagonalisation to have greater cardinality than that of S. However in 1897 Burali-Forti argued that the set of all possible sets must have the greatest cardinality.[§] A further technical difficulty with Cantor's ideas was raised by the French mathematician Richard. Richard's paradox contends that since all concepts are expressed using only finite sequences of symbols (e.g.

[†] The 'meaning' of formal propositions and how meaning is associated with notational calculi was the subject of much of Wittgenstein's work commencing with his famous *Tractatus Logico-philosophicus* (1918). A less technical development of the Theory of Meaning is presented in Russell's 1918 paper *On propositions: what they are and how they mean* (reprinted in *Logic and Knowledge - Essays 1901-1950* edited by R.C. Marsh, Allen and Unwin, 1984)

[‡] This is still true today. All careful treatments of set theory, even elementary ones, are careful in avoiding giving a rigorous formal definition of the term 'set'.

[§] The Burali-Forti paradox was originally formulated in a much more precise technical form. Modern theory resolves this, and related paradoxes, by not admitting the 'set of all possible sets' as a valid object (see [‡]).

sentences in the English language) it follows that only a countably infinite number of such expressions can be built. But if this is so and Cantor's analyses of set cardinality are valid how can uncountably infinite objects, like the real numbers, be described?

The apparent contradictions in Cantor's set theory, the existence of paradoxes in logic at a time when logic and set theory had become central ideas in proofs, and the precedent of modifying an established theory (Euclidean geometry) to yield an equally acceptable new theory; all these engendered doubts about how secure the foundations of mathematical reasoning and proof were. It was in an attempt to dispel these doubts that Hilbert's axiomatic approach and the *Entscheidungsproblem* were proposed.

It should be noted that the axiomatic school was only one of a number of groups attacking such questions. Two other important approaches were pursued.

1. *Logistic*: Frege, in work spanning 20 years, attempted to base mathematical reasoning solely on the manipulation of pure symbolic logic. Russell discovered a significant error in Frege's formalism and, in collaboration with Whitehead, attempted to correct Frege's approach. This work formed the basis of their book *Principia Mathematica* (3 volumes, unfinished).[†]

2. *Intuitionistic*: This group, led by the Dutch mathematician Brouwer, contended that the only admissible concepts in mathematical reasoning were those objects that could be constructed. Thus an algorithm could be found or *shown to exist* that defined the object. The Intuitionistic school also rejected the so-called 'Law of the Excluded Middle' i.e. the

---

[†] Ideas underlying this may be found in Russell's 1901 essay *The logic of relations*, which is reprinted in Marsh, *op. cit.*

axiom that for any predicate, P, it holds that $\neg(\neg P) \Rightarrow P$; this underpins the validity of 'proof by contradiction'; cf. our earlier proof of the undecidability of the halting problem in which we infer from the contradiction arising out of the existence of an always halting Turing machine solving the halting problem that no such machine exists.

Each of these approaches had problems: the logistic method never satisfactorily resolved the problem of logical paradoxes.[†] The Intuitionistic approach could resolve the Burali-Forti paradox, since the 'set of all sets' would not be a constructible object, but could not deal with the following objection: since all reasonable construction algorithms must have at worst a countably infinite number of steps how could the real numbers be admitted as a valid object.[‡]

In any event one might argue that both these approaches ultimately reduce to Hilbert's axiomatic framework: the starting propositions and rules for manipulation of these constitute the axioms and inference system for symbolic logic; similarly initial objects and construction rules play the same role in the intuitionistic method.

The refutation of all three approaches came in 1931 when the Austrian logician Kurt Gödel published his famous Incompleteness Theorem[§], that essentially shows that no set of axioms with properties P1 and P2 above could exist, and that thus Hilbert's program could not be written. Of course Gödel's results do not invalidate mathematics as an

---

† Russell's *Mathematical Logic as based on the Theory of Types* (1905) in (Marsh, *op. cit.*) attempts but ultimately fails to do this.
‡ This, of course, is just a variant of Richard's paradox.
§ Gödel, K: '*Über formal unentscheide Sätze der Principia Mathematica und verwandter Systeme, I*'; Monatshefte für Math. und Physik, 38, (1931), 173-198; (On provably undecidable propositions of the *Principia Mathematica* and related systems, I)

intellectual pursuit: to use an analogy with compilers, all experienced programmers are aware that any high-level language compiler they use *will* contain errors; however this does not mean that they cease to write software.

In the final chapter of this book we shall develop a simplified version of Gödel's result[†]. In this chapter we present a more formal framework in which to consider axiomatic systems and Hilbert's program. This is done with respect to a simple *language for arithmetic.*

Definition 9.1: The *language for arithmetic,* which is used subsequently, is the language L built from the following symbols:

1. Variables: $x, y, z \cdots$

2. Constants: **0, 1**

3. Operators: $\times$, **+**

4. Equality: =

5. Logical connectives: $\neg, \vee, \wedge, \Rightarrow, \Leftrightarrow$

6. Quantifiers: $\exists, \forall$

7. Punctuation: (,).

It should be noted that these are merely *formal symbols,* and that any interpretation may be placed on the operators $\times$ and **+**, the constants **0** and **1**. Since our concern is with arithmetic we shall be employing the specific interpretation that **0** and **1** are the integers 0 and 1; **+** and $\times$ the operations of addition and multiplication and variables take values over **N** $\cup$ {0}. Other interpretations are possible which would give rise to theories other than

---

† Our presentation is developed from the treatment given in Machtey, M; Young, P: (1978) *An Introduction to the General Theory of Algorithms,* North-Holland

arithmetic. •

The symbols of L are used to formulate a precise definition of 'assertion'.

Definition 9.2: The *terms* of L are inductively defined by the following rules:

T1. Variables and constants are terms.

T2. If s and t are terms, then so are $s + t$ and $s \times t$.

T3. All that are terms arise by reason of T1 and T2 alone.

The *formulae* of L are inductively defined by:

F1. If s and t are terms then $s = t$ is a formula.

F2. If F and G are formulae, then so are $\neg F$, $(F \vee G)$, $(F \wedge G)$, $(F \Rightarrow G)$, $(F \Leftrightarrow G)$, $\exists x\, F$ and $\forall x\, F$ for all variables x.

F3. All that are formulae arise by reason of F1 and F2 alone.

In formulae of the form $\exists x\, F$ and $\forall x\, F$, F is called the *scope* of x. Any occurrence of x in F is said to be *bound*. If a variable in a formula is not bound to any quantifier it said to be *free*. A formula that contains no free variable occurrences is called a *sentence of L*. Sentences are our formal model of 'mathematical assertions'. Thus under the arithmetic interpretation of the symbols of L sentences are either *true statements* or *false statements*. •

Example 9.1: The sentence

$$\forall x\ (\ \neg\ (x = 0)\ \Rightarrow\ \exists y\ (y + 1 = x)\ )$$

states that for any non-zero x there exists some natural number y such that $y + 1 = x$. In the usual arithmetic interpretation this sentence is true. •

It is important to understand the distinction between sentences that are *true* in the usual interpretation, and sentences that are *provably true*. It is not necessary to give a precise definition of the former; one can be inferred from the inductive definition of sentence. To capture the notion of proof we need to specify some means of deriving further (true) sentences from given true sentences. In accordance with the preceding discussion this involves describing a set of *axioms* which are taken as true. The following represent a (minimal) set of axioms for the language L.

$S1$ $0 + 1 = 1$

$S2$ $\neg (x + 1 = 0)$

$S3$ $\neg (x = 0) \Rightarrow \exists y (y + 1 = x)$

$S4$ $(x + 1 = y + 1) \Rightarrow x = y$

$T1$ $\exists y (y = x + 1 \lor x = y \lor x = y + 1)$

$A1$ $x + 0 = x$

$A2$ $x + (y + 1) = (x + y) + 1$

$M1$ $x \times 0 = 0$

$M2$ $x \times (y + 1) = (x \times y) + x$

This allows the following definition of *proof*.

Definition 9.3: Let S be a sentence of L and $A = \{A_1, \ldots, A_k\}$ a *finite* set of axioms for L (e.g. the set listed above). S is said to be *provable from A*, if the truth of S can be established from the axioms A alone[†]. A sentence S which is true in the arithmetic interpretation and provable from A is said to be a *theorem of the theory* (L,A). A sentence, S, which is false in the arithmetic interpretation and for which $\neg S$ is provable is said to be *logically invalid*. •

[†] Strictly speaking we should associate a finite set of *inference rules* with each axiom which states how sub-formulae in a given sentence may be replaced by another formulae in agreement with the axiom. This is rather tedious and it is clearer to assume some intuitive appreciation of what constitutes a proof using a finite axiom set alone.

So, for example, one can establish that $0 \neq 1$ from these axioms by observing that the assumption $0 = 1$ together with axiom S1 contradicts axiom S2.

With this formalism we have the following picture of the universe of sentences of L.

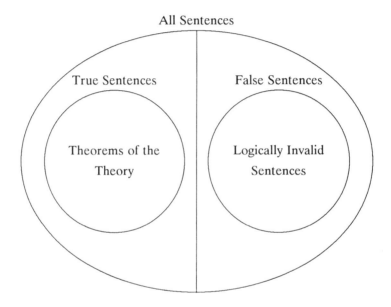

Now although our set of axioms is fairly weak (there are sentences that are true but not theorems) they are sufficient to *represent* the class of r.e. languages. For alphabet $\{0,1\}$ let w_n denote the nth word in the canonical ordering of words and for a r.e. language $L \subseteq \{0,1\}^*$ let $\chi_L : \{0,1\}^* \to \{0,1\}$ denote the characteristic function of L.

Definition 9.4: Let $Q \subseteq \{0,1\}^*$ be an r.e. language. Q is said to be *representable in* (L,A) if there is a formula $F_Q(x,z)$ (where x and z are variables of L) such that the sentences

$$F_Q(x,z) \wedge F_Q(x,y) \;\; \Rightarrow \;\; y = z \quad ; \quad F_Q(n,m)$$

are theorems of the theory (L,A), for all natural numbers n and $m \in \{0,1\}$ such that $\chi_Q(w_n) = m$.

Thus the first sentence asserts that the value of $\chi_Q(w_x)$ is unique; the second that the true sentence $\chi_Q(w_x) = m$ is a theorem. •

Theorem 9.1: For all r.e. languages, Q over $\{0,1\}$, Q is representable in the theory (L,A) described above. □

It follows from Theorem 9.1 that for any r.e. language Q if $\chi_Q(w_x) = m$ this fact is provable in the theory.

We conclude this section by describing the important properties which any theory should satisfy.

Definition 9.5: Let (L,A) be *any* mathematical theory, defined in the style presented above. (L,A) is *consistent* if and only if for all sentences S of L *at most one* of S, $\neg S$ is a theorem of the theory.

(L,A) is *complete* if and only if for all sentences S of L *at least one* of S, $\neg S$ is a theorem of the theory. •

In the next section we shall prove the following results of Gödel which have the effect of removing any possibility that Hilbert's program exists.

For any consistent 'sufficiently powerful' theory there is no algorithm for deciding whether or not arbitrary sentences of the theory are theorems.

Any consistent 'sufficiently powerful' theory in which the set of theorems is recursively enumerable, is not complete.

The meaning of 'sufficiently powerful' is left to the next section.

Chapter 10

Gödel´s Incompleteness Theorem

Il y a avait là un triomphe ... sur la facon dont il venait de mener à bien cette affaire compliquée et obscure: un chef-d'œuvre de fine analyse, disait-on, une reconstitution logique de la vérité, une création véritable, en un mot.

Emile Zola
La Bête Humaine

At the end of the previous chapter we showed that the simple language L for arithmetic together with a (fairly weak) set of axioms A was capable of expressing any r.e. language Q. Thus for any such language Q if $\chi_Q(w_n) = m$ then this fact could be represented by a *provably* true sentence of L.

Before proceeding with Gödel's results some facts from Chapter 4 are recalled, namely:

F1. There is a mapping

$$\gamma^{-1} : \mathbf{N} \longleftarrow r.e. \ languages$$

that associates some r.e. lanaguage with each natural number. Thus we can speak of an ordering of languages $Q_1, Q_2, \ldots,$ in which Q_n is the language recognised by the Turing machine whose code, $\beta(M)$, satifies $\gamma(\beta(M)) = n$.

F2. There is a universal language, Q_{univ} that is r.e.

F3. The sets $S_0 = \{w_n : w_n \notin Q_n\}$ and $S_1 = \{w_n : w_n \in Q_n\}$ are recursively inseparable, i.e. $S_0 \cap S_1 = \emptyset$ and there is no recursive set R such that $S_0 \subseteq R$, $S_1 \subseteq \{0,1\}^* - R$.

Let Q_{univ} be a universal language. From Theorem 9.1 and F2 there is some sentence of the theory L, $F_{univ}(x,y)$ that represents Q_{univ}. Using this sentence we can construct an infinite set of sentences $S(n)$ defined as follows.

For all $n \in \mathbf{N}$, $S(n)$ is the sentence

$$F_{univ}(2^{2n+1} + 2^n - 1, \ 0)$$

Lemma 10.1: The sentence $S(n)$ is true in the usual interpretation if and only if $w_n \notin L_n$.

Proof: Let $N(n) = 2^{2n+1} + 2^n - 1$. Then $w_{N(n)} = 0^n 1 0^n$ since there are exactly $2^{2n+1} - 1$ words whose length is less than $0^n 1 0^n$ and the only words of length $2n+1$ that can precede $0^n 1 0^n$ are those of the form $0^n 0x$ where $|x| = n$. There are exactly 2^n of these. The lemma now follows easily: $S(n)$ is the sentence $F_{univ}(N(n), 0)$; since F_{univ} represents Q_{univ} it is true in the usual interpretation if and only if $0^n 1 0^n \notin Q_{univ}$, i.e. if and only if $w_n \notin L_n$. $\square$

Let AX denote the sentence:

$$\forall x \ \forall y \ S1 \wedge S2 \wedge S3 \wedge S4 \wedge A1 \wedge A2 \wedge M1 \wedge M2 \wedge T1$$

So that AX is just a single sentence equivalent to the finite set of axioms (and therefore trivially true and provable).

Now Q_{univ} is a universal language, and so for any n

and m

$$0^n \, 1 \, 0^m \in Q_{univ} \quad \Longleftrightarrow \quad w_m \in L_n$$

Since F_{univ} represents Q_{univ} it follows that if $w_n \notin L_n$ then the sentence $F(N(n),0)$ is a theorem of the theory (L,A), i.e. provable. On the other hand if $w_n \in L_n$ then the sentences $F_{univ}(N(n),1)$ and $\forall \, w \; F_{univ}(N(n),w) \Rightarrow w = 1$ are theorems. So since $0 \neq 1$ is provable we have in total that if $w_n \in L_n$ then $\neg \, F_{univ}(N(n),0)$ is a theorem of the theory.

To summarise:

$$w_n \notin L_n \quad \Rightarrow \quad S(n) \; provable \; from \; A$$

$$w_n \in L_n \quad \Rightarrow \quad \neg \, S(n) \; provable \; from \; A$$

It follows that if $w_n \in L_n$ then the sentence $AX \wedge S(n)$ is logically invalid and if $w_n \in L_n$ then $AX \wedge S(n)$ is a theorem.

Finally we say a mathemetical theory, T, is *minimally adequate* if it contains all the symbols of L and the sentence AX above is a theorem of T.

Minimally adequate is our interpretation of the phrase "sufficiently powerful".

Theorem 10.1: (General Undecidability Theorem) For any minimally adequate theory there is no algorithm for recursively separating the theorems of the theory from the logically invalid sentences.

Proof: If $w_n \notin L_n$ then the sentence $AX \wedge S(n)$ is a theorem since the theory is minimally adequate and hence proves AX which proves $S(n)$. If $w_n \in L_n$ then the sentence $AX \wedge S(n)$ is logically invalid using the arguments preceding. It follows that any algorithm to separate theorems from invalid sentences would imply the existence of an algorithm to separate the sets S_0 and S_1 of F3. But this contradicts Theorem 4.4. □

An immediate corollary of this result is

Theorem 10.2: (Gödel Undecidability Theorem, for Theorems)
For any consistent, minimally adequate theory there is no
algorithm for deciding whether or not arbitrary sentences
are theorems of the theory.

Proof: If T is any consistent, minimally adequate theory then
the sets

$$TH = \{AX \wedge S(n) \ : \ w_n \notin L_n\}$$
$$LI = \{AX \wedge S(n) \ : \ w_n \in L_n\}$$

are disjoint and from the proof of the General Undecidability Theorem, are recursively inseparable. □

In practice one is only concerned with "reasonable"
theories, for which the axioms (and thereby inference rules)
are r.e. With such a condition the theorems of a theory
are r.e. by simply repeatedly applying the inference rules
to generate all provable sentences.

Theorem 10.3: (Gödel Incompleteness Theorem) Any consistent, minimally adequate theory, T, for which the
theorems of T are r.e., is incomplete.

Proof: Suppose T is a consistent, complete, minimally adequate theory whose theorems are r.e. From the assumption
that T is complete given any sentence S of T either S is a
theorem of T or $\neg S$ is a sentence of T. Since the
theorems of T are r.e. there exists an algorithm *SEP* which
given any sentence of T eventually halts and accepts if the
sentence is a theorem. However this implies that for any
sentence S we can determine whether S is a theorem or
logically invalid; simply simulate *SEP* on S and $\neg S$ alternating steps. This contradicts Gödel's Undecidability
Theorem (for theorems). □

All the preceding results apply to arbitrary interpretations of the symbols of L. For the specific instance of arithmetic, we have

Theorem 10.4: (Gödel Undecidability Theorem, for Truth) There is no algorithm for deciding whether arbitrary sentences of the Theory of Arithmetic over N and $(+, \times)$ are true or false. □

Exercise: Is the set of sentences which are true in the usual interpretation of L r.e.? Justify your answer. •

Theorem 10.4 shows that Hilbert's program does not exist. It might reasonably be argued that the construction of a class of undecidable sentences (the $S(n)$ of the General Undecidability Theorem) is artificial and that perhaps there are important open problems which could be resolved by mechanically finding a proof, e.g. Fermat's Theorem. In fact even this is too much to hope for. Work of Gödel in 1938 and Cohen in 1964 proves that *Cantor's Continuum Hypothesis* (Hilbert's First Problem) could not be decided using the accepted axioms of set theory alone.

Definition 10.2: Cantor's Continuum Hypothesis asserts that:

There is no infinite set with cardinality strictly greater than N and strictly less than R.

Fact 10.1: If Cantor's Continuum Hypothesis is accepted axiomatically as true in a consistent theory, then the resulting theory is still consistent. (Gödel)

If the negation of Cantor's Continuum Hypothesis is accepted axiomatically as true in a consistent theory, then the resulting theory is still consistent. (Cohen) □

In fact the foundations of arithmetic are potentially even weaker than is implied by this. It cannot even be shown that the axioms of arithmetic are *consistent*, using the arithmetic axioms alone.

Theorem 10.5: (Gödel, 1931) For any consistent, minimally adequate theory T of arithmetic such that the theorems of T are r.e., the consistency of T cannot be proved within T.

Proof: (Sketch) The proofs of T, i.e. finite sequences of inference rules applications, can be numbered (see the enumeration of Turing machine encodings in Chapter 4). This *arithmetisation or Gödel numbering* admits the construction of a sentence asserting

If I am provable then there is a shorter proof of my negation

□

Although the Theory of Arithmetic over **N** is undecidable, there are some effective algorithms for deciding the truth or falsity of sentences in some non-trivial theories. The following result was discovered by Presbürger in 1929.

Theorem 10.6: The Theory of Addition over **H** is decidable whenever **H** = **Z** (integers) or **Q** (rationals) or **R** (reals). The first is known as *Presbürger Arithmetic.* □

10.1. Discussion

It is easy to view Gödel's Incompleteness Theorem and Turing's undecidability results solely as negative conclusions about the power of their respective systems. In Chapter 9 I briefly described the circumstances in which Hilbert's *Entscheidungsproblem* was proposed and outlined the approaches taken to solve it — approaches that, ultimately, proved to be futile. It is sometimes claimed that this 'failure' in some way weakens or even invalidates mathematics as an intellectual or scientific activity. Indicative of such an underlying feeling are those arguments advanced in an attempt to counteract Gödel's proofs — in effect arguments that either seek to defend logic as a mathematical reasoning tool by selecting a definition of 'mathematical truth' within which the Incompleteness Theorem is not applicable, or — the opposite extreme — attack the use of symbolic logic as a basis of reasoning in mathematics. We find both positions being promoted by Wittgenstein writing between 1937 and 1942.

> I have constructed a proposition (...P...) · · · it can be so inter-
> preted that it says "P is not provable [in Russell's system†] · · · "
> Just as we ask: "'provable' in what system?", so we must also ask:
> "'true' in what system?". "True in Russell's system" means: proved
> in Russell's system; and "False in Russell's system" means: the
> opposite has been proved in Russell's system. Now what does
> "suppose it is false" mean? *In the Russell sense* it means that "sup-
> pose the opposite is proved in Russell's system"; *if that is your
> assumption*, you will now presumably give up the interpretation
> that it is unprovable · · · If you assume that the proposition is
> provable in Russell's system, that means it is true *in the Russell
> sense*, and the interpretation 'P is not provable' again has to be
> given up. If you assume that the proposition is true in the Russell
> sense, *the same* thing follows. · · · For what does it mean to
> say that P and 'P is unprovable' are the same proposition? It
> means that these *two* English sentences have a *single* expression in
> such-and-such a notation.
>
> Remarks on the Foundations of Mathematics
> I, Appendix III, paras. 8-9

> The harmful thing about logical technique is that it makes us for-
> get the special mathematical technique. · · · The curse of the
> invasion of mathematics by mathematical logic is that now any
> proposition can be represented in a mathematical symbolism and
> this makes us feel obliged to understand it. · · · 'Mathematical
> logic' has completely deformed the thinking of mathematicians
> · · · by setting up a superficial interpretation of the forms of
> our everyday language as an analysis of the structures of facts.

† i.e. the logical calculus of *Principia Mathematica*. [P.E.D.]

ibid.
V, paras. 24, 46, 48

I have quoted these extracts at length mainly to indicate the philosophical difficulties that Gödel's results presented. One should be wary of dismissing the arguments advanced above too readily. Let us consider the first extract (written *ca.* 1937) which may be summarised in the following contention: 'mathematical truth' is not an absolute entity but must be viewed relative to the formal systems in which mathematical assertions are proved — the 'true' propositions of a theory (L,A) are exactly those assertions that are provably true within (L,A).

If accepted this invalidates the Incompleteness Theorem since the proof centres on the construction of a sentence that asserts its own unprovability. Wittgenstein argues that one cannot move outside the formal system (whether Russell's calculus or our simplification developed in Chapter 9) in order to justify the 'truth' of such a proposition. Intuitively this does not sound convincing: if one is reasoning about properties of the natural numbers (i.e. the Theory of Arithmetic) it is possible that there are relationships that are valid (in that counterexamples could never be found) but that a sentence in an accepted logical calculus, asserting the validity of these relationships, may be unprovable. For example consider Fermat's Last Theorem: in a precise form this asserts the non-existence of four natural numbers x, y, z and n with a specific relationship, namely that $n \geq 3$ and $x^n + y^n = z^n$. Regardless of which formal system is adopted this proposition is either true (i.e. there are no such natural numbers) or it is false (i.e. a falsifying quadruple exists). If the theorem is true it is possible that it is not *provably* true in, for example, Russell's logic or some other calculus. Here mathematical truth is *independent* of a formal proof system.

There is, however, a sense in which Wittgenstein's argument appears to be acceptable. At the opening of Chapter 9 the parallel postulate of Euclidean geometry was described and, at the end of Chapter 10, Cantor's Continuum Hypothesis discussed. What can be said of the 'truth status' of either of these propositions? It cannot be argued that either is true (or false) in the absolute sense that Fermat's Last Theorem must be true or false. An answer is provided, in part, by Wittgenstein's contention that the 'truth' of, say, the parallel postulate is relative to the logical system in which it is being considered: thus (axiomatically and therefore provably) true in Euclidean geometry; (axiomatically and therefore provably) false in non-Euclidean geometries. In the same way, from Gödel's 1938 result, we have a (Cantorian) Theory of Sets in which the Continuum Hypothesis is true (again by virtue of its truth being an axiom of the system); from Cohen's 1964 result one can, in principle, define a (non-Cantorian) set theory in which the Continuum Hypothesis is (axiomatically) false. In both these cases the 'truth' of a (particular) proposition is implicitly linked to the axiomatic framework in which the proposition is asserted.

One might object that this separation of arithmetic and geometry as theories, for the purposes of differentiating concepts of truth external and internal to formal systems, is rather arbitrary. Nevertheless there is an important distinction that can be drawn between assertions such as Fermat's Last Theorem and Goldbach's Conjecture on the one hand, and the parallel postulate and Continuum Hypothesis on the other. The distinction concerns a 'one-sided' aspect of the former examples: it cannot be the case that the two arithmetic assertions are *unprovably* false since the languages corresponding to counterexemplifying instances are both r.e.

Thus if either proposition is false one may construct a program that will *eventually* deliver a counterexample. Supposing the status of the parallel postulate or Continuum Hypothesis were open, this argument would not apply: there are uncountably many choices of potential counterexamples to the parallel postulate (i.e. lines and points in the real plane) and a counterexemplifying set to the Continuum Hypothesis would have to be non-denumerable.

In the second extract (written *ca.* 1942) one finds a vituperative attack on the use of logic as a reasoning basis in mathematics. The criticism is based on two points: that techniques derived from logic are alien to mathematical thought; and that vague ideas can be given an apparently rigorous form by encoding them as propositions. It is difficult to argue against the first criticism — largely because Wittgenstein does not define what is meant by 'the special mathematical technique'. The second criticism appears to confuse the concepts of soundness of *syntax* and soundness of *semantics*. Symbolic logic as a mathematical tool is valid in terms of the syntactic derivation of further propositions consistent with axiomatic or established propositions. It would be a mistake, however, to assume that the symbol strings derived always represent 'sensible' propositions. In order for this to be true, at the very least, the initial axiomatic assertions must be semantically sensible. If one takes as a basis what is believed to be a 'propositional encoding' of an only vaguely understood concept then it will not be surprising if the deductions made as a consequence are apparently meaningless. In programming language terms the second objection is rather like criticising high-level languages such as Prolog on the grounds that they appear to impart 'intelligent behaviour' to computers whereas the results delivered by, for example, Knowledge based systems, are only as useful as the information upon which they operate.

A good defence of the position of symbolic logic in mathematics and an acceptance of what Gödel's theorems imply is given in several of Russell's works after *Principia Mathematica*.

> One result of the work we have been considering[†] is to dethrone mathematics from the lofty place that it has occupied since Pythagoras and Plato · · · thus mathematical knowledge ceases to be mysterious. It is all of the same nature as the 'great truth' that there are three feet in a yard.
>
> The Philosophy of Logical Analysis
> History of Western Philosophy, pp. 785-786

This passage takes a rather different view to the second excerpt quoted from Wittgenstein: far from allowing vague generalities to be given a spurious mathematicisation, the exploitation of logical calculi at the end of the 19th century was responsible for making precise some concepts that had previously been taken as intuitive. Russell contrasts the school of thought that arose from classical Greek mathematics with the formalistic concerns of later mathematicians. On one side the mystic quasi-religious view of mathematical concepts taken by Pythagoras and his adherents with its attribution of supernatural properties to numbers such as 1, 2, 3, 6 and 7 (cf. *Rev.*; 13:18); and its identification of number theory and numerology, of astronomy and astrology: attitudes that survived as late as the seventeenth century (cf. Kepler's *Somnium*); on the other side a concern for technical detail and precision. He notes

---

† The paragraphs preceding this excerpt discuss the increasing formalisation of mathematical concepts arising from the work of Frege and others.

that the 'philosophical' approach to mathematics led to a lack of rigorous definition in, amongst other areas, geometry, arithmetic and analysis. Russell then goes on to observe how the contributions of Lobachevsky (geometry), Weierstrasse (analysis), Cantor (cardinality and number) and Frege (arithmetic) produced a sounder technical basis for mathematical reasoning. Thus in a later essay written in 1950,

> Let us enumerate a few of the errors that infected mathematics in the time of Hegel. There was no definition of irrational numbers, and consequently no ground for the Cartesian assumption that the position of any point in space could be defined by three numerical coordinates, There was no definition of continuity, and no known method of dealing with the paradoxes of infinite number. The accepted proofs of fundamental propositions in the differential and integral calculus were all fallacious $\cdots$ As regards geometry, it was supposed that the truth of the Euclidean system could be known without any appeal to observation. The resulting puzzles were all cleared up during the nineteenth century, not by heroic philosophical doctrines such as that of Kant or that of Hegel, but by patient attention to detail.

Logical Positivism
Logic and Knowledge: Essays 1901-1950, p. 369

In summary Gödel's result on consistency and completeness in formal systems may be viewed as the culmination of this process of dephilosophising mathematics: to this extent the results are a positive contribution to mathematical thought. To attribute some mystic significance to the fact that there exist unprovable assertions in formal systems is as irrational as making similar claims for the facts that π is transcendental[†] (i.e. squaring the circle is impossible) or that there are

---

[†] Some of the reactions to this fact are surprising: even as late as 1927 one finds groups such as the Indiana State Congress passing legislation 'decreeing' that π equals three and that this value was to be employed for the purposes of all calculations carried out within the state's jurisdiction e.g. in

three feet in a yard. In Russell's essay, from which I quoted earlier, the interaction of mathematics and philosophy post-Gödel is summarised succinctly:

> There has been a vast technical development of logic · · · Not that difficulties are at an end. A new set of puzzles has resulted from the work of Gödel · · · in which he proved that in any formal system it is possible to construct sentences of which the truth or falsehood cannot be decided within the system.
>
> This whole subject has become so technical · · · that it can hardly be regarded as belonging to philosophy as formerly understood. True, it solves what *were* philosophical problems, but so did Newton in writing on what he still called 'natural philosophy'. But we do not now regard planetary theory as part of philosophy, and I think that on the same ground much of the recent work on logic, syntax and semantics should be regarded as definite knowledge, not philosophical speculation.
>
> Logical Positivism
> Logic and Knowledge: Essays 1901-1950, pp. 371-2

schools, universities and engineering applications.

Chapter 11

Computer Science and Computability Theory

11.1. Introduction

The preceding chapters of this book have considered the subject of computability largely as a mathematical discipline. In this, concluding, chapter we shall examine the wider relevance of this area to the field of Computer Science as a whole.

We have seen that one of the central concepts of computability theory is the idea of a *model of computation*. There is considerable flexibility in how such models may be defined — from simple string processing systems to analogues of stored program computers to application of simple mathematical operators to a set of basis functions — and yet this diversity of definitions does not exhibit any difference with respect to the class of problems that are solvable within each formalism. The use of an abstract model to reason about properties of 'real' systems is, of course, a fundamental scientific method. The genesis of such models in the study of computability can thus be viewed as a significant foundation in the development of Computer Science as a scientific discipline. One can trace the continuation of this approach in divers aspects of Computer Science such as: Computational Complexity Theory (which addresses the question of the quantitative resources — e.g. time and space — required to solve specific problems and so must provide modelling definitions of these resources); semantics of programming languages with its corresponding application to formal verification of programs; simulation of computer systems; design of computer architectures; etc.

11.2. The Church-Turing hypothesis

The Church-Turing hypothesis asserting the equivalence of all 'reasonable' models of computation to Turing machines provides a unifying basis for the claim that if a problem cannot be solved on *some* model then it cannot be solved on any 'practical' computer architecture. There are a number of popular misconceptions about the Church-Turing hypothesis (as indeed there about the consequences of Gödel's results). Since certain of these recur in the (less technical) literature it is as well to be aware of them.

One of the most common sources of misinterpretation has been the field of what may be called non-von Neumann architectures: e.g. massively parallel computers, neural networks, quantum computers, etc. Are such models 'reasonable' and if so do any violate the Church-Turing hypothesis? Consider quantum computation which was introduced in the work of Deutsch (1985)[†]. This model is sometimes

---

† Deutsch, D: (1985) Quantum theory, the Church-Turing principle and the universal quantum computer; *Proc. R. Soc. Lond., Series A*, 400, 97-117

(wrongly) claimed to be capable of solving problems that Turing machines (and other reasonable models) cannot solve. This misrepresentation is not due to Deutsch who states in the abstract to the paper cited:

> A class of model computing machines that is the quantum generalization of the class of Turing machines is described, and it is shown that quantum theory and the 'universal quantum computer' are *compatible with the [Church-Turing] principle*. Computing machines resembling the universal quantum computer could, in principle, be built and would have many remarkable properties not reproducible by any Turing machine. These do *not* include the computation of non-recursive functions · · · (my italics)

Some of the literature on quantum computation has claimed the opposite while citing Deutsch (1985) as supporting evidence.

The cases of parallel machines and neural networks are rather more interesting and similar. Recall Exercise 3.4 above in which a model of computation based on Boolean logic expressions was defined. It can be shown that there are 'programs' within this model capable of solving *any* decision problem. If models of computation encompassing parallel computation and neural machines are defined in a general enough way then the property of being genuinely universal (i.e. capable of solving any decision problem) would also apply to these formalisms (by using similar reasoning). There is, however, a powerful argument for regarding such models as being 'unreasonable' and therefore the Church-Turing hypothesis is not invalidated by them. This argument is based on the property of computational models called *uniformity*. A proof that the model of Exercise 3.4 can solve any decision problem might go as follows.

Consider any language $L \subseteq \{0,1\}^*$. There are a finite number of words of length n in L (at most 2^n). Thus we can define a Boolean function, f_n, of n arguments, $<x_1, \ldots, x_n>$ such that

$$f(\alpha_1, \ldots, \alpha_n) = 1 \quad \Longleftrightarrow \quad \alpha_1 \alpha_2 \cdots \alpha_n \in L$$

Given the statement of Exercise 3.4 we can now construct an appropriate Boolean expression to compute this function.

Now in a *uniform* model a *single, finite* program is specified which must deal with *all* possible inputs. In a *non-uniform* model a *different* (finite) program may be specified for each different input size. The important point about a non-uniform program (sequence) is that the instance to deal with inputs of size 100, say, need be of no use at all in constructing the instance to deal with inputs of size 101.

Non-uniformity violates the notion of 'reasonable model' since it only indicates that a program sequence to solve, for example, the halting problem for Turing machines, *exists* (within the model). Obviously the program sequence is infinite so one cannot write down every single program instance in the sequence. Furthermore one cannot explicitly construct this sequence, for if there were a single finite program which given n as input returned the nth Boolean expression used, then this program could be simulated by a Turing machine. Failure to appreciate this subtlety has resulted in 'models which disprove the Church-Turing hypothesis' being announced in some of the (fringe or popular) literature. In all such cases the error is usually found to be that of comparing a non-uniform model with a uniform one.

The misconceptions outlined in the preceding paragraphs arise from the assumption that the Church-Turing hypothesis overstates its case. At the other extreme are errors in understanding the precise circumstances in which some machine-based decision problems are undecidable. If we take the halting problem as an example, this may be instantiated for Turing machines — as was done earlier — or for other models of computation. Suppose that P is some programming system, not necessarily capable of simulating Turing machines. We may define the halting problem for P in an obvious way: given a program p belonging to the system, and an input x for p, does p halt when started with input x? A stronger version might insist that the problem be solved within the system P itself. We have seen that if $P = Turing\ machines$ or $P = Post\ machines$ then the problem is undecidable. It is not the case, however, that the halting problem is undecidable for every programming system e.g. it is clearly trivial for the class of **goto**-free programs where it may be solved by a **goto**-free program. The problem is also decidable for less trivial models. For example if we consider a Turing machine model in which only $f(n)$ tape cells may be used during the computation on inputs of length n (where $f(n)$ is bounded) then the halting problem for '$f(n)$-bounded Turing machines' is decidable by (normal) Turing machines since there are only $3^{f(n)} \mid Q \mid f(n)$ possible instantaneous descriptions for such machines, and thus a simulation of the machine could be carried out which records each instantaneous description arising; if one should occur twice before the simulation halts then the bounded machine cannot halt on its input since it is looping. It may be observed that the simulation given here may itself be performed by a (larger) space-bounded Turing machine since an $f(n)$-bounded machine needs at most $g(f(n))$ different states for some bounded function g.

A similar fallacy is occasionally encountered in work on

knowledge based systems with respect to Gödel's results. Here it is assumed that since Gödel establishes the incompleteness of one particular theory it follows that *all* systems of axioms are incomplete with respect to the theory they apply to. As we remarked at the end of Chapter 10 there are non-trivial theories — Presbürger arithmetic for example — in which the truth of sentences is decidable. One may find literature in which it is stated that a particular knowledge base cannot been shown to be consistent and complete because of Gödel's results despite the fact that these are not relevant to the domain being considered by the knowledge base.

11.3. Computability Theory applied in Computer Science

We have argued that the concept of a model of computation, introduced in computability studies, provides an important basis for other fields of Computer Science, fields whose applicability in practice is generally accepted: thus computational complexity and the study of algorithms is well-motivated by the fact that efficient methods of solving problems will always be of interest regardless of technological advances; and the study of formal methods, such as verification and specification techniques, increases in significance as progressively more complex programs are proposed and developed. It may appear that computability theory as a subject does not have such importance. Two common arguments used to support the claim that computability issues are not relevant to 'practical' Computer Science may be loosely summarised by the following contentions.

1. Many (all?) of the problems that are known to be undecidable are not problems that arise in 'real' applications. Therefore the fact that there are undecidable problems is of no practical interest.

2.   Since all existing computers are *finite* resource machines we can in effect always solve the specific instances of machine-based decision problems that arise e.g. the halting problem for computer architecture X is decidable.

The first contention actually makes two claims, using the former to support the latter. Even if the assertion that "undecidable problems do not arise in 'real' applications" is accepted, one may argue that the inferred consequence "the existence of undecidable problems is of no practical interest" should not be. It could be said of Theorem 5.1 that its significance is not that it proves *the halting problem* to be undecidable but that it proves the halting problem to be *undecidable*. That is to say the achievements of Computability Theory are not (primarily) in showing that some specific single computational problem is incapable of solution by algorithmic means, but in the provision of a battery of reasoning techniques by which whole classes of problem can be considered. Whether one agrees with this or not, in any event, there are numerous examples of undecidable problems that do arise in 'real' applications and so the initial premise is unfounded. To see this we can consider two cases: one in a very general appplication area and one in a specific domain. Earlier we referred to the problem of validating knowledge bases for consistency and completeness. Notwithstanding the cases referred to previously, there are instances where researchers have correctly identified specific knowledge bases as being incomplete. In this case there arise problems — can assertion P be verified from the data in knowledge base S? — that are undecidable. In this situation undecidability does matter in practice since the users of such systems have to be aware of the fact that queries made of the knowledge base *may* be unresolvable. As the

second example, there are problems arising in the design of
document management systems that are known to be undecidable. The interested reader is referred to Bench-Capon
and Dunne (1989)[†] for a more detailed description of these.

Turning now to the second contention, one can put
forward a number of objections. First of all, it only refers
to decision problems concerning properties of programs. In
the case of other decision problems, such as determining
the validity of a given assertion within a logical system or
the matrix mortality problems, the argument does not apply:
one can only hope to solve finite restrictions of these; e.g.
does this assertion have a proof containing at most f steps;
or can this instance of the mortality problem be solved
using a product of at most k matrices. Secondly, although
one certainly *could* solve the halting problem for programs
running on any specific real machine just by adapting the
argument given earlier for $f(n)$-bounded Turing machines, it
may be shown that any such solution for a specific machine
M could not be implemented on machine M — it would
require an architecture with greater memory capacity. Furthermore one could not construct a general program that
would solve the problem for all finite resource machines in
a specific class of architectures.

In summary Computability Theory is of importance to
Computer Science as a discipline since: it introduces the
concept of modelling computation by an abstract formalism;
it has developed a pool of techniques by which computational problems can be classified, e.g. reducibility between
different problems; and, although in practice it is more

---

† Bench-Capon, T.J.M; Dunne, P.E.S: (1989) Some computational properties of a model for electronic documents; *Electronic Publishing*, 2 (4),
231-256

common for a problem to be intractable because of the resource needs of the best algorithms available, it provides the awareness that effective algorithms may not always exist.

11.4. Further reading

The treatment of computability theory developed in the main chapters of this book serves only as a basic introduction to the subject. The reader interested in pursuing this area in greater depth may find more extensive treatments in the books of Cutland (1980), Hopcroft and Ullman (1979), and Machtey and Young (1978).

Rogers (1967) is probably the most comprehensive treatment of recursive function theory. Manna (1974) gives a good overview of other aspects of theoretical computer science.

Cutland, N.J: (1980) *Computability*; Cambridge Univ. Press

Hopcroft, J.E; Ullman, J.D: (1979) *Introduction to Automata Theory, Languages and Computation*; Addison-Wesley

Machtey, M; Young, P: (1978) *An Introduction to the General Theory of Algorithms*; North-Holland

Manna, Z: (1974) *Mathematical Theory of Computation*; McGraw-Hill

Rogers, H: (1967) *Theory of Recursive Functions and Effective Computability*; McGraw-Hill

Index

LIVERPOOL
UNIVERSITY
LIBRARY